INDIANS

POCAHONTAS, *Seymour*
PONTIAC, *Peckham*
SACAGAWEA, *Seymour*
SEQUOYAH, *Snow*
SITTING BULL, *Stevens*
SQUANTO, *Stevenson*
TECUMSEH, *Stevenson*

WILBUR AND ORVILLE WRIGHT,
Stevenson
WILL AND CHARLIE MAYO,
Hammontree

UNIVERSITY SCHOOL
LIBRARY
KENT, OHIO

Juv Coll PZ 7 .D658 Le

Dobler, Lavinia G

Lee de Forest, electronics
boy.

NAVAL HER

DAVID FARRAGUT, *L*
GEORGE DEWEY, *Lon*
JOHN PAUL JONES, *S*
MATTHEW CALBRAITH
OLIVER HAZARD PER
RAPHAEL SEMMES, *Sm*
STEPHEN DECATUR, *S*

NOTED WIV
and MOTHE

ABIGAIL ADAMS, *Wa*
DOLLY MADISON, *M*
JESSIE FREMONT, *Wa*
MARTHA WASHINGTO
MARY TODD LINCOL
NANCY HANKS, *Steve*
RACHEL JACKSON, *Co*

ALBERT EINSTEIN,
ALECK BELL, *Widd*
CYRUS MCCORMICK
ELI WHITNEY, *Snou*
ELIAS HOWE, *Corco*
ELIZABETH BLACKW
GAIL BORDEN, *Par*
GEORGE CARVER, *S*
GEORGE EASTMAN,
GEORGE PULLMAN,
GEORGE WESTINGH
HENRY FORD, *Aird*
JOHN AUDUBON, *M*
JOHN BURROUGHS,
JOHN DEERE, *Bare*
LUTHER BURBANK,
MARIA MITCHELL, *N*
ROBERT FULTON, *H*
SAMUEL MORSE, *Sno*
TOM EDISON, *Guthr*
WALTER REED, *Higg*

WITHDRAWN FROM KENT STATE
UNIVERSITY LIBRARIES

UNIVERSITY SCHOOL
LIBRARY

D1379449

THEM FROM THE POCKET

Lee de Forest

Electronics Boy

Illustrated by William Moyers

Lee de Forest

Electronics Boy

By Lavinia Dobler

THE **BOBBS-MERRILL** COMPANY, INC.
A SUBSIDIARY OF HOWARD W. SAMS & CO., INC.
Publishers • INDIANAPOLIS • NEW YORK

UNIVERSITY SCHOOL
LIBRARY
KENT, OHIO

USL
J
B
D315d

COPYRIGHT © 1965, BY LAVINIA DOBLER

ALL RIGHTS RESERVED

PROTECTED UNDER UNIVERSAL COPYRIGHT CONVENTION

AND PAN-AMERICAN CONVENTION

LIBRARY OF CONGRESS CATALOG CARD NUMBER: 65-23667

PRINTED IN THE UNITED STATES OF AMERICA

UNIVERSITY SCHOOL
LIBRARY
KENT, OHIO

For my cousins
Lavinia and Forrest Brouhard
and
John, Linda and Sandra Brouhard

446973

Illustrations

Full Pages

Numerous smaller illustrations

Contents

★ ★

Books by Lavinia Dobler

CYRUS McCORMICK: FARMER BOY
LEE DE FOREST: ELECTRONICS BOY

★ Lee de Forest

Electronics Boy

The Talking Machine

LEE DE FOREST jumped over the cracks of the board sidewalk. He was walking down Main Street with his mother in Waterloo, Iowa, where he lived as a boy.

Suddenly he stopped and listened. Someone with a high voice was reciting,

> Mary had a little lamb,
> Its fleece was white as snow.

Five-year-old Lee was puzzled. He knew most of the Mother Goose rhymes, and this one was his favorite. He wondered who was talking.

He glanced at the people on the wide sidewalk. Maybe it was the man with the tall black

11

hat, who was standing in front of one of the stores. Lee hurried over to a white building with a big glass window. The man with the stovepipe hat walked on down the street. The reciting went on, and the words seemed clearer than they had been before.

And everywhere that Mary went,

The lamb was sure to go.

Lee bubbled up with laughter and put his hand over his mouth. It sounded so funny to hear the words and not to see the person who was saying them.

"Lee," Mrs. de Forest called to her young son from farther up the street. "Hurry up," she said a trifle impatiently as she shifted her heavy bundles. "We must get home."

"Mama, I can't." Lee shook his head. "I have to find out who's reciting 'Mary Had a Little Lamb.' I think he's in this store." He pointed to the newly painted building.

"We're already late," his mother said. "We must hurry. I promised your sister we would not be gone very long."

"I can't go inside that big store alone," Lee pleaded. "Please come with me."

"Well, come along then," sighed Mrs. de Forest, adjusting the heavy bundles again. "I might as well come, because you won't be satisfied until you find out." The flowing skirt of her long gray dress dragged on the ground as she retraced her steps.

"I have to find out, Mama," Lee insisted.

"Your middle name should be Inquisitive." Mrs. de Forest smiled at her son.

Together they entered the shop. On the long oak table Lee saw an odd-looking machine with a brass and iron base. A cylinder with a shiny silvery cover was going round and round. A man with a black mustache stood nearby, turning a crank to make the cylinder go.

13

"The machine is doing the talking!" Lee exclaimed, his blue eyes getting bigger.

The man with the fancy mustache laughed pleasantly. "You're right, son," he said.

"A talking machine?" Mrs. de Forest asked.

The man nodded. "It's a phonograph invented by Thomas Edison of New Jersey."

By this time Lee had walked around the machine several times. He listened even more closely to the words.

Mary had a little lamb.

He was thrilled with the wonder of it. "How does the voice come out?" he asked.

Before the man could answer, Lee asked another question. "Who's talking about Mary and her little lamb?" he inquired.

"Mr. Edison, the great inventor," the man said. "His voice is recorded on the cylinder. This machine reproduces the human voice." The man pointed to the cylinder. "This cylinder is

14

covered with tin foil. When the cylinder goes round, this needle follows tiny grooves in the tin foil. Then you hear Mr. Edison's voice."

Lee put his ear close to the disk. He thought he could hear the delicate sound the needle made as it followed the tiny grooves.

"The machine looks simple," Mrs. de Forest said, "but I don't understand how it works." She seemed as interested as her son.

"I wish we could have one," said Lee, looking up at his mother.

"This one is not for sale," the man in the shop said. "It's only on exhibit."

"Oh," said Lee. He was disappointed. He studied the machine again. He wished he could see what was inside the cylinder. He looked up at the man and smiled.

"Maybe when I'm older, I can make one, or something like it," he said hopefully.

"One of these days almost every home will have a phonograph," the man said. He looked directly at Lee as he spoke. "We need more inventors like Mr. Edison to help make our lives richer and happier."

"Thank you, sir, for showing us this talking machine," said Mrs. de Forest. "We must hurry

16

home now." She walked with Lee toward the door of the shop. The man smiled and hurried to open the door for them.

"Thank you, sir," Lee said politely. "I want to come back soon to hear the man say 'Mary Had a Little Lamb.' May I?"

"Yes." The man nodded. "Maybe your father would like to come with you."

"I want Papa to see the talking machine—I mean the phonograph." Lee said the new word proudly. "Good-by."

The little boy waved as he and his mother walked down the street. He could hardly wait to get home and tell his father about the phonograph. He wondered what his father would say about this amazing machine.

The de Forest home with big shade trees and a green velvet lawn was one of the most attractive places on the block. Lee ran across the yard and opened the front door.

"Papa," he called eagerly. There was no answer, so he ran down the hall to the library. "Papa," he called again.

The boy was disappointed because he couldn't find his father. The Reverend Henry Swift de Forest was the minister of the Congregational Church in Waterloo. He spent much time at his oak desk in the library. Sometimes he read to his son from the books that had shiny gold letters on the leather backs.

Lee decided that his father had left the library, possibly to visit a member of the church who was ill. He might not return home until suppertime, and Lee could hardly wait to talk with him about the phonograph.

Lee started to leave the room. Suddenly he heard a rustling sound and quickly turned around. A yellow head peeked from behind the dark, old-fashioned sofa.

"Guess who!" squealed his sister Mary.

18

"Oh, it's you," said Lee. "You know Papa doesn't want us to be in his study when he's not here. Come on out."

"All right, Lee," Mary said agreeably, "if you will come with me."

Lee took his sister's soft, warm hand, and together they left the library. He wanted to tell her about the phonograph, but knew that she wouldn't listen. She seemed to be interested only in dolls and doll clothes.

"Tell Mama I'm going over to Tom's house," he called to Mary as he headed for the back door. He hoped some of the boys in the neighborhood would be with Tom.

The big boys called Lee "Puny" because he was small for his age. He did not like to be teased in this way, but couldn't do anything about it. The boys were so much older and stronger than he, that he knew better than to protest or to try to fight them.

His mother had made him memorize the verse:

> Sticks and stones
> Will break my bones
> But names and faces
> Will never hurt me.

Sometimes it made him feel better. Sometimes it didn't. Today Lee could tell the big boys about the wonderful talking machine.

"Hello," Lee shouted to the boys who were playing ball in Tom's back yard.

"Hi," Tom called in return.

"I've just seen and heard a wonderful machine that talks," Lee said proudly.

"What's so special about that?" asked a tall boy with straight black hair.

"It talks the way you and I do," Lee explained. "It even says 'Mary Had a Little Lamb.' "

"Who wants to hear about Mary's little lamb?" one of the boys snickered. Then all the boys began to laugh.

20

"Does the machine really talk?" Tom asked.

"Yes, it does." Lee nodded.

"I'd like to see it," Tom said. "Come on, fellows. Let's go see it."

"Where is this wonderful machine that talks?" the tallest boy asked.

"It's in a shop on Main Street."

"The owner of the shop will probably chase us out," said one of the boys. "Most storekeepers don't like to have people come in unless they buy something."

"I want to hear this machine that talks," Tom insisted. "Let's go."

"Well, all right," the tall boy agreed.

When the boys were only a few blocks from Main Street, they heard a train whistle. "I'll bet there are a lot of freight cars on the tracks today," shouted the tallest boy, who was also the oldest. "Let's forget about Lee's machine and go to the railroad depot."

"Yes, let's go," said another. "It will be more exciting to watch a train than to see that talking machine." The boys dashed off, headed for the railroad station.

Lee stood on the corner alone, watching the boys race down the street. "Tom," he called, "you said you wanted to see the talking machine. Come with me."

Tom turned around. He hesitated for a minute and took a step or two toward Lee. Then, without saying anything, he ran in the opposite direction to catch up with the big boys.

Lee walked slowly toward the railroad station. He was not supposed to go there by himself. He had been told to stay away from the railroad station and the railroad tracks. Mr. de Forest was strict with his children and sometimes punished them for disobeying.

"I'm not going," Lee said to himself. "It won't be any fun to see the train."

Lee looked once more in the direction of the depot before he started home. If he didn't join the boys, they probably would call him a 'fraidy cat, but he wouldn't mind.

Lee's parents had promised to take him to the circus, and the circus was tomorrow. He had never attended a circus, and he wanted very much to see the animals and clowns.

He started to run. Surely his father was home by now. He could hardly wait to tell him about the wonderful phonograph. By the time he opened the back door and rushed into the kitchen, he was breathless.

"Is Papa here?" he asked his mother.

"Yes, he's in the library," she answered.

"I want to tell him about the talking machine," said Lee, hurrying toward the study.

Mr. de Forest looked up from his papers and books as Lee came into the library. "Hello son," he said, smiling at the small boy.

"Mama and I saw the most wonderful machine today," Lee burst out excitedly. "It talks! It's called a phonograph." He told his father all about the talking machine.

"Phonograph comes from the Greek words for sound and writing," his father said thoughtfully. "This machine must record the human voice and other sounds."

"That's what it does," Lee said, pleased that his father knew so much about it. "I wish we could buy the phonograph, but it is only on exhibit." Lee said the word exhibit slowly, because he had never used it before.

"Then the phonograph is not for sale," Mr. de Forest remarked.

"Maybe someday I can make one," Lee said dreamily, "or something like it."

"A scientist with a background in physics would make a better one," his father said. "We are a family of ministers and teachers."

24

"Someday I'm sure I'll be able to make one," Lee insisted. "Or maybe I can invent something even better for people to enjoy."

"Your mother and I want you to study to be a minister or teacher," his father said firmly.

Just then Lee heard a strange kind of music coming through the open bay window. He raced over to the window to look out.

"I've never heard music like that before," said Lee. "Why does it sound so exciting and different from other music?"

"Someone is playing a calliope," Mr. de Forest explained. "No circus is complete without this strange musical instrument." Mr. de Forest seemed to be as interested as his son.

"Papa, we really are going to the circus, aren't we?" Lee asked.

"Yes, son," replied Mr. de Forest.

"I can hardly wait until tomorrow," Lee said breathlessly.

The Big Circus

THE NEXT MORNING Lee woke up before the rooster in the neighbor's back yard started to crow. As he lay in bed, looking up at the high ceiling, he thought about the elephants and the lions and the calliope.

He wanted to talk to Mary about the circus, but she was still sound asleep. The quilts hid all but the top of her curly head.

At last Lee heard his mother in the kitchen and knew that he would be permitted to get up. He jumped out of bed, dressed quickly, and looked at himself in a big mirror. He combed his tousled straw-colored hair to straighten out some of the waves. This was an important day and he wanted to be well-groomed.

"Mama," he called as he skipped down the stairs into the kitchen, "I'm all ready for the circus."

"Good morning, son. Why, you've even combed your hair." She smiled as she hugged him. "You are early. It will be several hours, before the circus parade starts."

"I can't wait," said Lee impatiently.

"The time will go much faster if you keep busy," she said calmly. "Breakfast will be ready soon, but I need more wood for the fire. Please bring some from the shed."

"All right, Mama," Lee said slowly. Keeping the woodbox filled was one of his duties.

When he returned to the kitchen with the wood, he smelled sausage frying. "Are we having pancakes?" he asked, his mouth watering. He felt very hungry just now.

"Sausages and pancakes for my favorite boy," his mother answered merrily.

When the de Forests finally left the house to see the parade, they were dressed in their best clothes. Lee wore short navy blue trousers and a starched white shirt with a big bow. He and Mary both wore straw sailor hats. Lee's hat had a wide black band and Mary's had a red ribbon that hung in long streamers.

Lee pointed to the gay-colored poster on the side of an old wooden building. "Will the elephants be as big as they look in that picture?" he asked his mother.

"Bigger than that," she assured him.

The de Forests heard music long before they reached Main Street, and Lee began to worry. He feared they were late.

"What if the parade is already over?" he asked anxiously. "I hear music. The parade must be going on now."

28

When the de Forests reached Main Street, a band was marching by in the parade. Lee stared at the beautiful red and gold uniforms which the members wore and at the shiny brass instruments which they carried. His hands and feet kept time to the lively music, and his heart beat fast with excitement. He had never seen anything like this before.

Right behind the band came a team of handsome matched horses, each wearing a rich harness trimmed with silver and gold. The horses were pulling a huge cage mounted on wheels. In the cage was a drowsy lion.

"The lion looks sleepy," said Lee. "I wish he would roar."

"He probably would rather sleep than be in a parade," said Mr. de Forest. "However, if he opened his mouth and roared, he would scare a lot of boys and girls."

"I wouldn't be afraid," Lee boasted.

Another big red and gold cage, almost like the first, contained a tiger. Lee watched, fascinated, as the huge cat paced back and forth. What if this great black and yellow animal got loose and sprang at the crowd?

At last several big clumsy elephants with flopping ears came marching by. Lee opened his eyes wider than ever. He had known that the elephants would be big and clumsy, but somehow he had expected them to be different.

"What big ears they have!" he exclaimed.

Each elephant had a small platform strapped on its back. The platform was covered with a sort of canopy which made it look like a little house. A man or woman sat in a seat on each platform and waved at the people.

"What are those things on the backs of the elephants?" Lee asked.

"They are called howdahs," explained Mr. de Forest. "In India, where many people ride elephants instead of horses, howdahs take the place of saddles."

"Look at the pretty, pretty ladies!" Mary squealed joyfully. The ladies were sitting or standing on the backs of horses, prancing along the street. Each lady was very graceful and wore a sparkling costume.

A sour-faced clown dressed in pantaloons stumbled along beside the horses. He turned cartwheels and then bowed, first to people on the right, and then to people on the left along the street. Men, women, and children roared with delight at his antics.

"Why doesn't the clown laugh?" asked Lee.

"He seems funnier because he never laughs or smiles," said Mr. de Forest.

Lee looked more closely at the clown to see whether or not he ever smiled. The clown's face never even broke into a smile, yet the crowd laughed at everything he did.

31

Lee watched every circus performer and every animal in the parade with delight, but he was more interested in the shrill tunes of the calliope, than anything else.

"How does the calliope work?" he asked.

"I don't think I can explain it," Mr. de Forest replied. "Maybe we can ask the man who plays the calliope."

"I hope so," Lee said eagerly.

"Since this is Circus Day," Mrs. de Forest said, "we'll eat on the circus grounds and then watch the performance in the big tent."

"That'll be fun," Mary and Lee chorused.

The circus grounds were in a big empty field across the railroad tracks. The de Forests left Main Street and started for the grounds. Lee was silent as they walked past the railroad tracks. How glad he was that he had run home yesterday instead of following the other boys. He clutched his father's hand tight.

32

Hundreds of people were milling around the noisy circus grounds. Everyone seemed to be having a good time. The harsh music from the calliope fascinated Lee.

"I'm curious to see how that calliope works," he told his father.

The family walked over to the bright-colored music machine. Lee noticed a large boiler at one end. He wanted to ask a question, but he suddenly felt very shy. He pulled on his father's coat sleeve.

"Papa, please ask the man."

Mr. de Forest touched his son's shoulder. "Of course." Then turning to the man, he said, "Pardon, Mister, will you please tell us how the calliope works?"

The man nodded pleasantly, but kept on playing. A few minutes later, when he found an opportunity to rest, he said, "We have to keep feeding charcoal into the firebox to build up steam. It takes a lot of steam to play twenty-one whistles."

"This calliope is much larger than the phonograph," Lee said to himself.

"We have to have more than 120 pounds of steam pressure to make the whistles blow with the correct pitch. If we let the pressure go down, the whistles have a lower pitch and the music doesn't sound right."

"You mean the music sounds flat," Mrs. de Forest spoke up.

"That's right!" the man chuckled. "If you look closer, you can see that the keys on the keyboard are connected to valves on the whistles by wires and arms. Then when I play the keys, we have music, glorious music."

The man wiped his forehead and went on playing. Lee looked at the keys and noticed that they were similar to those on a piano.

The harsh sounds of the calliope seemed

louder than ever. Lee put his hands over his ears to muffle the sounds.

"I hope my son understands your explanation," said Mr. de Forest. "You've been very kind. Thank you, sir."

"Don't mention it," the man answered.

As the de Forests headed for the big tent, Lee's father asked, "Do you understand now how the calliope works?"

"Yes, I think so," Lee said happily.

"You certainly are more curious about mechanical things than I am," said Mr. de Forest.

The huge tent was almost filled by the time the de Forest family sat down with the crowd to watch. Children nearby were waving flags. One almost hit Mary in the eye.

Lee had never seen a trapeze act before. He held his breath while beautiful ladies in pink tights swung from one trapeze to another, high in the top of the tent.

Both Lee and Mary liked to watch the clowns with their painted faces, big red mouths, and oversized noses. They laughed loudly as the clowns turned somersaults and pushed one another over without smiling or saying a word. Some of the clowns even stood on their heads and winked at the children.

The crowd roared and applauded all the circus acts. Lee clapped his hands with the rest. After the performance he wanted to see the events in the side tents, but his mother said, "We can't afford any extras."

Mary and Lee had pennies with which to buy pink popcorn and bright red balloons. "What's inside the balloons?" asked Lee.

"Hydrogen," the vendor answered.

Many boys and girls cried because their gay balloons burst. Lee carried his balloon carefully in front of him to protect it. He wanted to keep it for a long time.

Just as they walked into their own front yard, Mary's balloon touched a limb of a tree. There was a loud pop.

"My balloon! It's gone!" Mary sobbed.

"You can play with mine," Lee offered. He was grateful that his was all right.

The family had a light supper and shortly afterwards Mary and Lee went upstairs to bed. As soon as they were alone, Mary whispered, "Let's have a circus of our own."

They moved the beds to one side and turned somersaults and stood on their heads. They made so much noise that their mother came upstairs to quiet them down. Lee's red balloon floated to the ceiling. He could not reach it. "I'll get it tomorrow," he thought sleepily.

The next morning he found his balloon on the floor under the bed. "Why did it come down?" he asked. "Some of the hydrogen must have leaked out and let it come down."

"Mama, where is the circus today?" Lee asked at breakfast that morning.

"It left Waterloo by train during the night for some other town in Iowa," she said.

"Then I'll have to wait a whole year to see and hear the calliope again."

"Maybe longer than that," his mother said. "We are moving to Muscatine where your Grandfather Robbin lives."

"I don't want to move," Lee protested.

"Your father must go where he is needed," Mrs. de Forest said reprovingly. "We believe God will show us the right way."

From Muscatine to Talladega

IN THE year 1878, the de Forest family moved to Muscatine, Iowa. There they lived in a red brick house directly across the street from Grandfather Robbins' home.

Lee loved his grandfather, a kindly gentleman with fine silver hair. Mr. Robbins had been one of the founders of Muscatine. Years before, he had left Massachusetts and traveled hundreds of miles by stagecoach and river boats to reach the Iowa Territory.

He had come to preach the gospel to settlers in a new land. He had established one of the first churches in Muscatine, and was still the beloved pastor of this church. After coming here, he had found many ways to help people, and the people were very fond of him. They trusted him as a friend.

A few days after the de Forest family arrived in the new town, Grandfather Robbins said to Lee, "Now you are living in Muscatine, which is on the Mississippi River. You should learn to spell *Mississippi*."

"Miss-iss-ipp-i," said Lee, spelling the word slowly aloud for his grandfather. "Mississippi is a long word, but very easy to spell." He spelled *Mississippi* again—this time much faster than before.

His grandfather laughed. "Yes, Mississippi is easy to spell," he said. "Some words in our language are mighty hard to spell."

Lee was not old enough to attend school, and there were no children nearby for him to play with. Only at Sunday School did he see boys and girls regularly. He really missed his friends at Waterloo.

Sometimes he went to see Grandfather Robbins, but he felt timid around Grandmother Robbins, who was really his stepgrandmother. She peered at him with cold blue eyes through steel-rimmed spectacles, and made him feel uneasy.

Inside the house, Grandmother Robbins always seemed to be watching him. Often he felt guilty, when he had done nothing wrong.

Lee was fascinated with a sugar bowl, which his grandmother kept on a shelf in a china closet. This bowl was filled with lumps of sugar and was decorated with beautiful pink flowers.

Time after time Lee stood and gazed at the pretty sugar bowl. He knew that it was filled with lumps of sugar which he called candy. Always he was afraid to ask for some.

One day he waited until Grandmother Robbins went to the kitchen. Then he tiptoed over to the china closet and looked at the pretty bowl. He tried to open the glass door of the china closet, but it stuck. Just at this moment, his grandmother walked into the room.

"What are you doing?" she asked sharply.

Lee couldn't think of anything to say. He looked at the floor and didn't answer.

"You were trying to get my china bowl and might have broken it," she said. "Even though you are a little boy, you must learn to leave people's things alone. Go home now." She pointed to the door.

Lee hung his head and walked slowly out of the room. He was hurt by being sent home, but he was more hurt because his grandmother had called him a little boy. He felt as miserable as when the big boys in Waterloo had called him Puny.

Lee went to his room in the brick house,

closed the door, and hid his face in the pillow. He had been foolish to try to reach the pretty bowl. Now his grandmother thought that he was a bad boy. She might even punish him farther by not letting him come to his grandfather's study. He buried his head deeper in the feather pillow.

A few days later Grandfather Robbins came over to the de Forest home. Lee and Mary were playing in the back yard.

"Lee," his grandfather called, "I have a surprise for Mary and you upstairs in my study." His gray eyes twinkled.

"A surprise?" Lee asked.

Grandfather Robbins nodded. "Would you like to come with me?"

"Yes, Grandpa," Lee said happily, "if it's all right for me to come."

Of course it's all right for you to come," Mr. Robbins assured his grandson.

"I'll run and tell Mama," Lee said.

"I've already arranged for you to come," Mr. Robbins said. "Come on, both of you."

Lee greeted his grandmother politely as they entered the house. Then he quickly followed Mr. Robbins and Mary up the stairs to the pleasant, book-lined study.

"I've arranged a treasure hunt," Grandfather Robbins announced as soon as he had closed the oak door. "I've hidden some goodies. Now you may look for them."

"What fun!" Mary said gleefully.

Lee and Mary found nuts and candies in the oddest places, behind books on the shelves, under the leather pillow in the big chair, and even under the scatter rugs.

Lee discovered a stick of horehound candy beside an oil lamp on the desk. He forgot about the candy because he became interested in looking at the oil inside the glass base.

He could not understand how the oil in the lamp rose up on the wick so that it could be burned. He asked his grandfather, but Mr. Robbins shook his head.

"I can't tell you, my boy." Then his eyes brightened. "Now if you asked me a question about religion, I could answer it. You know, we are a long line of ministers, and probably you will be a minister, too."

Lee realized that his grandfather, like his father, expected him to be a minister. Right now he was only interested in finding how the oil rose in the lamp.

Later in the afternoon, after the treasure hunt, Lee and Mary sat on the opposite arms of the big chair with Grandfather Robbins seated between them. Then Grandfather read them the story of David and Goliath from the Bible. Lee looked at him and thought he had a very nice grandfather and a very wise one, too.

Lee was never to forget the long cold winter the family spent in Muscatine. One morning when he went outdoors to play, he was fascinated with the silvery white deposit of ice needles that had formed during the night. Even the iron latches of the kitchen door were covered.

Lee was so excited at the beautiful sight that he called to the housemaid in the kitchen. "It's like magic. Why even the latches are covered with snow!" he exclaimed.

The maid came to the door. "That's not snow," she corrected him. "It's a kind of frost."

Now the maid didn't like children and thought it would be fun to play a trick on Lee. "If you put your tongue on the latch, you will hear the angels sing," she said.

"That's strange," said Lee.

He looked at the maid and then at the latch again. He didn't know whether to believe the maid or not. He waited and looked.

"Why don't you try it?" the maid asked. "I guess you just don't believe me."

Lee boldly put his tongue on the latch. To his dismay, it stuck to the surface just as if it were glued there. Part of the skin came off when he pulled it away. Lee couldn't understand. The latch was cold, but his tongue felt as if it had been burned.

"Mary, don't put your tongue on the latch," he said, holding his hand over his mouth to ease the pain. "What a strange trick!"

Lee ran into the house to tell his mother what the maid had done. She had made him angry, but he also had bothered her with questions about the frost. Suddenly he stopped and returned to join Mary outside.

Before long the maid left the de Forest home to work for a family with no children. Lee was not sorry to see her go.

A few days later Lee heard his parents talking

seriously together in low voices. His father said that he wanted to do something about the plight of freedmen in the South. He said that they needed help.

Lee knew about the War between the States. He knew that the Negroes who had once been slaves were now free men.

These days Mr. de Forest was unusually sharp and impatient. Lee tried to be good, but every now and then he did something annoying. Then he was punished, sometimes severely.

Finally Mrs. de Forest asked Mary and Lee not to bother their father in the library. "He is worried," she told them. "He is trying to decide what to do about the future."

"Are we going to move away from Muscatine?" Lee asked his mother.

"Maybe," she answered. "We may go to live in a place far away from here."

Soon Mr. de Forest received word that he had

50

been elected President of Talladega College, a school for Negroes, in Talladega, Alabama.

"This is what I want most to do," Mr. de Forest said. "There is a big job to be done, and those people need me." Lee's father was over six feet tall, but now he looked even taller to the little boy. What faith his father had!

"How many times have we moved?" Lee asked.

"When you were born in 1873, we lived in Council Bluffs, Iowa," said Mrs. de Forest. "First we moved to Waterloo and second to Muscatine. Now before long we'll move to Talladega, Alabama." There was a light in her blue eyes as she went on. "I think probably we'll live a long, long time in Talladega."

The trip on the train from Iowa to Alabama was long and dreary. Lee was tired and sleepy on the train. "Mama, when will we get there?" he asked wearily.

"We're almost there," Mrs. de Forest said. She was holding Lee's baby brother, Charles, who had been born shortly before the family left Muscatine.

In a few moments Mr. de Forest helped his wife and three children alight from the sooty day coach of the train. They stood on the platform near the rust-colored wooden depot of Talladega, Alabama.

"Good day, Mr. de Forest," said a man with a pleasant smile. "Wecome to Talladega." The two men shook hands.

"We have a two-seated buckboard buggy for you to ride in," the man said, "and an empty wagon to hold the baggage."

Lee never forgot the ride from the depot to the college. As they jogged along on the unpaved streets, he looked with interest at the village square, the houses, and the people.

Bricks for Stone Hall

"I WISH Papa would come home," Lee said one day to his mother. "I miss him very much when he is away."

"Your father is doing the kind of work that he loves," Mrs. de Forest explained to Lee. "He works long hours to improve the school, whether he is here at home or whether he is traveling. He tries to solve every problem that arises, no matter how difficult."

"Why does he have to work so hard?"

"He wants to help the freedmen," Mrs. de Forest explained. "In this way he believes that he is best serving the Lord."

Lee's father often had to be away from home for long periods of time. During these trips he raised money for the school.

The school depended largely on contributions from people in the North who wanted to help the Negroes. Many more students were enrolled than before, and the school greatly needed classrooms and dormitories.

A short time later, Mr. de Forest returned from a trip to the New England states. He told his family about a wealthy woman he had met, named Mrs. Valeria Stone.

"Mrs. Stone is deeply interested in the fine work we are doing here at Talladega and has given us a generous amount of money," said Mr. de Forest. "I'm suggesting that we call our new boys' dormitory Stone Hall in honor of this noble woman." Lee noticed that his father's eyes were bright as he talked about Mrs. Stone and the new building.

"Yes, of course, the new building should be named for her," Lee's mother agreed.

Less than two years after the de Forests moved to Talladega, the new building was started. The bricks for the building were made nearby, because the red clay in the ground was good for making bricks. The same kind of bricks had been used in erecting another building at the school. This building had been erected prior to the War between the States.

Lee was really excited about the new building. Week after week, he watched the men and boys, many of them students at Talladega, mould the soft bricks and lay them on the ground to dry. They placed the bricks neatly side by side in long rows.

Lee's father had warned him to keep out of the way of the workers. Lee was curious, however, to watch all the steps in brickmaking. One day when the brickmakers were busy elsewhere, he touched a brick that had just been moulded. It felt soft and moist somewhat like the mud pies his sister made.

He pressed the brick, not realizing that his fingers would make little dents in the clay. Then he looked at the dents in dismay and tried to make the clay smooth again. He made them less noticeable, but he could still see them.

Like his father, he was anxious to have Stone Hall beautiful in every way. He smoothed the brick again. It looked a little better, but the marks still showed slightly.

Just then he heard the lunch bell ring. His mother was expecting him to come promptly. He couldn't stay there any longer.

Lee could hardly eat his lunch because he was so worried about what he had done. After lunch, he hurried back and found that the brick had dried. He looked closely, but no longer could see the little dents.

After the bricks dried, the workers stacked them in tunnels to be fired or baked. Lee watched the workers carefully.

"Are you building a pyramid?" he asked.

"No, but we arrange the bricks in the shape of a triangle," the young student answered. "We stack the bricks in layers, but each layer has less bricks than the layer beneath. The base has to be strong enough to hold the bricks which are piled on top." Then he smiled. "More on the bottom, less on the top—just like a triangle."

It took the workers some time to build up the great mound of bricks. Then they burned huge pitch-pine logs to bake the bricks and to make them strong and red.

The fire was even more colorful at night, when the flames leaped out of the tunnel mouths and through the crevices to the top. Lee noticed that the bricks on the bottom row were almost white from the intense heat.

Charles, who was five years younger than Lee, watched the fire curl around the bricks for a little while. Then he became restless.

"Let's play Indians," he begged.

"Go on if you want to," Lee answered without taking his eyes from the great log fire. "It's mysterious the way the heat changes soft clay into bricks as sturdy as rocks."

"All I can see is the big fire," Charles said impatiently, "and it's hot."

"The fire has to be hot to make the bricks hard," Lee explained patiently. "The bricks were made of soft clay—the kind that seems soft after a rain. This heat coming up through the holes will dry the water out of the bricks and bake them. Then the bricks will be hard and strong."

"I don't care," Charles said. "I want to play instead of just looking at a fire."

John, the man who was keeping a watchful

eye on the fire, walked over to where the two boys were standing. Lee turned to him.

"How strong will these bricks be?"

"Mighty strong, son," John said. "They'll be strong enough to resist both fire and weather. They will be as hard as stone."

"Stone Hall will last forever," said Lee.

John scratched his head. "Unless we have an earthquake, a flood, a hurricane, a tornado, or another war," he said. "We'll just hope and pray that nothing will destroy it. We've waited a long time to get this building."

Even though Lee had never met Mrs. Stone, who had generously given funds for the building, he knew that she must be a kind woman. It impressed him that the building was being named for her family. How nice it would be, he thought, if someday a building could be named for his family.

Little did he realize that, twenty years later,

another red brick building on the campus would be called de Forest Chapel. It would be dedicated in memory of his father, after nearly twenty years service as President.

Lee's father told him there would be a special ceremony when the cornerstone of Stone Hall was laid. "Sometimes a valuable book or historical paper is sealed inside the stone," he explained. "This time, however, we have chosen some things that we grow here at the school."

"What have you chosen?" Lee was excited.

"Suppose you guess," his father suggested. "I'll give you some clues. They are bright red, and you like them."

"Apples?" asked Lee.

Mr. de Forest shook his head. "Guess again."

Lee thought for a long time. "Cherries?"

"No, try again."

"Strawberries!" he exclaimed.

"You're right," said Mr. de Forest.

On a hot, sunny afternoon in May, Stone Hall was dedicated. Lee wore his dark blue serge suit and a crisply starched white shirt. For a while the stiff collar of his shirt made him uncomfortable.

When the ceremony started, Lee became so interested in the jar of bright red strawberries, preserved in alcohol, that he forgot his discomfort. These strawberries were to be placed in the cornerstone of Stone Hall.

The strawberries brought back happy memories to Lee. Sometimes, after dark, he would go alone to a strawberry patch nearby and pick a handful of the juicy, sweet berries. He wished he had some of them now.

He looked up at the blue sky overhead and then at the cornerstone. He knew that he would always be proud of Stone Hall. In a way, he felt that he was helping to build it.

New Home
and a Castle

FOR TWO years the de Forests lived in two small rooms on the second floor of one of the college buildings. They ate their meals in the big dining room on the first floor.

When the family sat down at the dinner table one evening, Mr. de Forest seemed to be more relaxed than usual. His eyes twinkled, showing that he was greatly pleased about something. Lee was curious to know why his father was so happy, but didn't ask any questions.

After Mr. de Forest had said grace, he smiled at his wife and three children. "I have especially good news for you," he announced. "This afternoon I received an important letter from some friends, who are going to give us a wonderful present. They are going to provide us with a new home."

"Yes, that is a wonderful present for us," said Mrs. de Forest. Her eyes were filled with tears but she was smiling. "We surely have many thoughtful friends. How can we ever repay them for their kindness?"

"Where will we build the new house?" Lee asked eagerly.

"Across the street in the center of the two-acre tract," his father answered.

"That's close to the strawberry patch," Lee said approvingly.

"Will I have a room of my own?" asked Mary.

"Will the house be made of brick?" Lee wanted to know.

"You ask questions faster than I can answer them," Mr. de Forest protested. "Yes, Mary, you will have a room of your own." Turning to Lee, he said, "The house will be made of bricks. Fortunately there are enough bricks left over from Stone Hall to build it." Mr. de Forest said *our house* with great pride.

"A whole brick house of our own!" Charles exclaimed. "That suits me."

Lee was nearly ten years old when the de Forest family moved across the street into their new red brick home. The yard had a picket fence on two sides. The rest of the yard was enclosed with barbed wire.

During their first summer in their home the de Forests had difficulty getting enough water. Water was stored in an iron tank in the attic and in a cement cistern back of the house.

Rain water from the roof flowed into the tank in the attic. The roof had steep slopes and wide gutters at the lower edge for catching the water, whenever it rained.

Several weeks went by, however, without any rain. First the tank in the attic became empty and soon there was no water in the cistern. The drought continued, and the de Forests were desperate for water.

A number of farmers nearby worked for the school. These men hitched mules to wagons and brought large wooden barrels of water to the de Forest home.

Lee did not like the water in the wooden barrels. "It doesn't taste like water," he told his mother. "I don't want to drink it."

"That is the only water we can get," Mrs. de Forest answered. "We must be grateful to have water at all."

A neighbor, Professor Andrews, had a deep well back of his house. When Lee wanted a cool drink of water, he often went over to this neighbor's house. One hot afternoon he started over there to get a drink of water.

66

Before he had gone very far, Charles came running after him. "Lee, where are you going?" the younger boy asked.

"I'm going over to Professor Andrews' house to get a drink of cold water from the well."

"I'm thirsty, too," Charles said.

Lee waited. Sometimes he objected to having his small brother follow him, but he realized that he should be patient. After all, he was the only brother little Charles had.

"All right," Lee called, trying not to sound cross. "Come along."

Charles ran to catch up with his brother. Together the two boys started to walk across a field to the Andrews home. When they reached there, the Andrews family was gone.

Lee was disappointed. He hesitated to take a drink from the well without asking. It was a hot day, however, and his throat was so dry he could hardly swallow.

Lee had never pulled up the oaken bucket by himself, but he felt sure that he could, and besides Charles could help him. The two brothers looked into the well and saw their faces reflected on the water.

"There are people down there," said Charles.

"No, you only see our shadows," said Lee.

Charles looked again. "We don't look like that, do we?" He seemed disturbed.

Lee laughed. "Those are our shadows," he explained. "The sun's behind us."

The boys had to work hard to pull up the bucket of cold water. There was a small house over the well, but there still was danger of falling in. They had to pull hard and to watch carefully at the same time.

They drank the clear water from a big tin dipper that hung by the well. Lee still felt worried because he did not have Professor Andrews' permission to get the water.

The boys each had three drinks of the cold water and Lee carefully replaced the dipper on the stone wall. The spot was shady and cool, but he knew he should go home.

"It's time to start home," he said.

"I don't want to go," said Charles. "Let's stay here where it's cool."

"We must go before our parents start looking for us," said Lee. He started to walk slowly down the path. A few minutes later Charles caught up with him.

Suddenly Lee stopped. "Did you have another drink of water?" he asked.

"Yes, I did," answered Charles. "I was still thirsty. I wish we had a well."

"Where did you put the dipper?"

"I left it in the bucket."

"Oh no," said Lee. "Is that where you found it when you got it?"

"No," Charles answered slowly.

Lee turned around and stared at his brother. "You must go back and put the dipper on the stone wall," he said. "That's the place where Professor Andrews always keeps it."

"It's too hot to go back and besides, Professor Andrews can find it," said Charles.

"If we don't leave the dipper where Professor Andrews keeps it," Lee said firmly, "then we can't expect to go back for another drink of cold water. We want to go back."

"All right! I'll go," said Charles, slowly retracing his steps. He placed the dipper on the stone wall and smiled as he caught up with Lee. "Now can we go back again when we are thirsty?" he asked.

Lee often had hard times finding things to do when there was no school. He knew very few children in town, and the few he did know were not very friendly. Some of the boys took delight in calling the de Forest boys "Yankees." Lee

70

couldn't quite understand why they were called this name.

The de Forest children had few friends their own age, but they had a close companion in their father. Mr. de Forest loved the outdoors. Nearly every Sunday after a big chicken dinner, he took his family for a walk. Often as he walked through the country, he talked seriously with the children.

Sometimes he let the children ask questions which he attempted to answer, but at other times he told them things that he wanted them to know. One morning he talked with them about some of the problems they would face later in life and about different kinds of people they would be sure to meet.

"If I study science," Lee said, "maybe I will invent something that will give people a better chance to understand one another."

"That is fine," his father said, "but right now

and later on, too, you must be kind to people. Don't argue or fight with them, even if you don't agree with them. Look for the good qualities in everyone."

Just then Charles, who was directly in front of Lee stooped down and picked a buttercup. He held it proudly in his chubby fist. "Brother," he said, "look at this flower. It's the color of the sun."

"It's the color of butter, too," said Lee, bending down to pick up another buttercup. Then he held the flower under Charles' chin and asked him whether he liked butter.

The boy giggled. "It tickles."

"Yes, you really like butter," Lee said.

"Bread and butter and strawberry jam," Charles laughed. "Maybe Mother will give us some later on. I'm getting hungry."

"We'll ask her," Lee said. He decided that his small brother was not so bad after all.

The three de Forest children had more freedom in their own home than they had in the dormitory. Now they could run and play in the house and outdoors in the big yard.

Fortunately, Lee liked to read. Recently he had become interested in knights and castles. One day when he was reading about King Arthur, he suddenly thought of what fun it would be to build a castle.

He went to the library shelf and looked for pictures of castles. He found some good illustrations of castles with moats, drawbridges, and turrets. He hurried down the hall.

"Mary! Charles!" he called.

When they came running, he asked eagerly, "How would you like to play knights?"

"I'd like to," Charles said promptly.

"You can be Lancelot," Lee told Charles. "Mary, you can be Elaine and I'll be King Arthur. How would you like that?"

"I want to be King Arthur," said Charles.

Lee had taken for granted that he would be King Arthur. He was older than Charles and thought that he should be the king.

"It's my idea," said Lee.

"I want to be King Arthur," Charles repeated. "I don't want to be Lancelot."

The two boys argued for quite some time. Then Lee suddenly burst out laughing.

"We don't even have a castle yet," he said, "so we don't have to decide right now who will be the ruler. Come on. Let's look for materials to make a castle."

The three children searched in the cellar for scraps of wood that had been left from building the house. They had carried the scraps to the cellar so that they would have them to use later during their playtime.

They spent a long time studying the pictures of castles in books. At first they wanted to

build an English castle, but they couldn't find a good picture to follow.

"Let's make the kind of castle that we want," Mary suggested.

"Yes, that's a good idea," said Lee, "but let's make it large enough so that we can move around inside."

The castle took longer to build than they had expected. Before it was completed, they had many practice battles. At Lee's suggestion, they called it Castle de Luxembourg.

"That sounds foreign and important," Mary said, repeating the words several times.

They found the little tower, or turret, quite hard to build. At first, they tried to make the tower round, but had to give up. Finally they made it square.

They built a moat about a foot deep and three times as wide. Water was scarce most of the time, however, and they had to imagine that the moat was filled with water. One day it rained and they hurried to get buckets to catch water to pour into the moat. Soon the moat was filled with water.

Next they worked on the drawbridge. After much figuring and struggling they finally had one that would raise and lower.

"When the drawbridge is closed, the Castle de Luxembourg can't be taken," said Lee. "It is cut off from the world."

"Yes, King Arthur," said Charles.

Lee and Charles made wooden swords to use in fighting battles. They took turns at being the Black Knight and other princely characters in books. Then one day Mary rebelled.

"I don't want to be Guinevere or Elaine any more," she complained. "I want to be a knight, like you and Charles."

"You're a girl, so you can't be a knight," Charles tried to explain to her.

"Then I won't play," said Mary, leaving the castle and walking slowly toward the house. The boys suddenly realized that they wouldn't have much fun playing without her.

"Come back," Lee called, running to get her. "You'll make a good Black Knight."

"Of course I will," said Mary. She smiled and came back to the castle.

Each day the children had new ideas for the castle. Once they used a big cracker box to make a new chest for King Arthur's tin armor. Then with much ceremony they put the armor in the Great Hall of the castle.

All too soon September came and the children returned to school. At first they were unhappy because they had had a happy vacation. They wondered whether they would ever have time again to play in the Castle de Luxembourg.

"This was the best summer I've ever had," said Mary, and the boys agreed with her.

Brilliant Stars
in the Sky

ON SUMMER nights when the heat was almost unbearable, Lee sat with his family on the lawn and looked up at the stars. Mr. de Forest pointed out some of the constellations in the heavens to his three children. He had studied astronomy in college and had always been interested in the stars.

"The Little Bear is the same constellation as the Little Dipper," Mr. de Forest explained. "If you look for a ladle with a long handle, you can easily find the Little Dipper. The North Star is the big bright star in the tip of the handle of the dipper."

Lee got up out of his chair and stood near his father. "Is the North Star at the very end of the handle of the dipper?" he asked. He gazed intently up at the blinking stars in the clear black sky.

"Son, you have sharp eyes," said Mr. de Forest proudly. He was pleased that Lee had found the groups of stars so quickly. "That sparkling star is the North Star. I use it as my guide to find other constellations."

"Where's the North Star?" Mary asked. She bent her head back as far as she could, trying hard to see the star.

Lee pointed. "Mary," he said, "look beyond my finger and you'll see it."

She walked over to where her brother was standing. Lee helped her to raise her arm to point in the direction of the star.

"Why, there it is!" She was as excited as Lee. "That's easy to find." She stood there a long time. Then suddenly she said, "Now I see all of the handle and the bowl. It's fun, Papa, to look at stars in the sky."

"Astronomy is a wonderful science," Mr. de Forest said. "It is one of the oldest, too. People studied the stars thousands of years ago and told stories about them."

"There are so many stars," Lee exclaimed. He moved his head from one side to the other, still studying the heavens.

His father laughed softly. "Yes, son, there are not only thousands of stars, there are millions of them."

"That many?" asked Lee, amazed.

"Yes, there are millions of stars only, of course, we can't see all of them."

"You mean that there are many stars in the sky that we can't see." He was trying to think what his father meant.

"That's right," Mr. de Forest said. "We can

hardly realize that there are many stars in the sky that we can't see with the naked eye. If we had a powerful telescope, we could see more of them.

"One very interesting constellation is the Milky Way," his father went on, pointing upward. "The stars in this constellation form a white streak across the black sky."

"You mean the stars that look like a white ribbon way up there?" Lee asked.

"He means all those stars up there that look like milk," said Mary.

"Let me see," said Charles. He hadn't shown any interest in the stars until now.

"I'll show you," said Lee. "Look for stars that help to make a white path almost across the sky." He took his brother's finger and pointed it in the direction of the band of sparkling stars far away.

"That is the Milky Way," he said.

"So that's the Milky Way," repeated Charles.

He suddenly seemed to be greatly interested in the stars. "Are all those stars very big?" He looked up at the sky intently.

"In the Milky Way," Mr. de Forest explained, "there are all kinds of stars."

Lee's eyes brightened. "Maybe some day," he said dreamily, "I can learn more about the Milky Way and all the stars."

"I hope so, son," Mr. de Forest said kindly. "I'm sure that you will." There was a note of encouragement in his voice.

That evening Mr. de Forest told the children about comets that shoot across the sky. The children listened closely to every word.

"For centuries," explained Mr. de Forest, "comets were considered omens of death and destruction. An omen is something that warns of, or fortells, a future event."

"Like a prophecy," Lee spoke up.

Mr. de Forest nodded and went on. "Years

ago people feared comets, because they looked like flaming torches flying across the sky. People often wore charms to keep from being hurt by comets."

Lee spoke up, "Once you told me that comets have tails."

"They surely do," said Mr. de Forest, chuckling. "Some of them have tails more than a million miles long flashing across the sky."

"That long?" exclaimed Mary.

Her father nodded. "Yes, some of their tails are millions of miles long."

"I'd like to see one," said Lee.

"You probably will sometime," Mr. de Forest answered. "Astronomers keep records of comets and can tell when they will appear again. They announce when to look for one."

After this conversation Lee was really excited when he had an opportunity to see a comet. "That is the fastest thing I ever saw," he said breathlessly. "I hope I'm still living when another comet comes!"

After this, Lee read several books from his father's library about comets. He felt that they were great mysteries in the sky and wanted to understand them better.

On hot days, Charles and Lee often walked through the woods to a river, where they knew of a good place to swim. The place was shaded by a large oak tree with broad branches extending out over the water.

One August day Lee and Charles ducked each other for a while in the cool, shallow water. After a while Lee grew tired of playing with his brother, and started to swim across to the other bank. Charles looked in surprise, knowing that he couldn't follow.

"That isn't fair," he shouted as he watched Lee swim farther away. "I can't swim, so I can't follow you."

Lee kept on swimming across the stream, using the dog paddle. He thought it was fun to swim in the deeper part of the river. Somehow he felt stronger in deep water, and his whole body tingled with the exercise.

"Please come back, Lee," Charles called again. "I can't swim after you."

For a while Lee tried to pretend that he couldn't hear his brother, but he finally turned and swam back to where Charles was standing. "It's time you learned to swim," he said. "Come on, and I'll teach you."

"I want to swim just the way you do," Charles declared. "Tell me what to do first."

Lee was flattered. He felt big and important when his younger brother looked up to him. Also he felt that Charles would learn quickly, because he wasn't afraid of water.

"I swim the way a dog does," Lee explained, "using a dog paddle. We'll stay here in the shal-

low water. Move your arms and legs the way I tell you, and I'll hold you up!"

"You won't let go of me?" Charles asked. He did not seem very confident now.

"Of course I won't let go of you," said Lee. "I'm your brother."

"You're my big brother, and you're the best swimmer I know," Charles declared.

Lee didn't know when he had felt so strong. Sometimes he really appreciated having a small brother. He put his hands under Charles' stomach to support him. Charles moved his arms and legs up and down. The water splashed over them, but neither boy minded.

"That's the idea," Lee said. "Keep using the dog paddle." He was greatly pleased with his brother's progress. "Moving your arms and legs keeps you going in the water."

"This is fun!" Charles said excitedly. "Will you help me every day till I can swim?"

"You'll be a good swimmer by the end of the summer," said Lee.

Lee and Charles were so interested in the swimming lesson that they failed to see some big boys standing under one of the oaks laughing at them. Finally Lee saw them.

"This is better than a circus," said one.

"See that puny boy, trying to hold his brother up," said another. "He's so puny that he'll drown if he isn't careful."

Whenever anyone called Lee puny, he wanted to fight, but knew that it wouldn't do any good. Now he simply led Charles toward the bank to pick up their clothes.

"My brother is not puny," Charles shouted to the big boys, ready to defend Lee.

"I say he is puny," the boy repeated.

Lee turned to his brother. "Get your clothes, so we can leave for home."

"This is our swimming hole," Charles argued.

"Hurry up," Lee said firmly. "Grab your clothes. You can dress somewhere else."

The hot sun beat down on the boys, but they ran fast to the college campus. Both boys were angry about what the strange boys had said. Lee wasn't tall for his age, but he could scarcely be called a weakling.

"Maybe I'll never learn to swim," Charles said sadly as he stopped for a second to catch his breath. "Can we go back to the river again after this happened?"

"Sure we can," Lee said. "Come on. We're almost home. Let's go into the study and tell Papa what happened."

Mr. de Forest listened quietly as his sons burst out with the story. After they had finished, he sat thoughtfully for a few minutes without saying a word. Then he drew his chair closer to the boys as if he had something important and helpful to say.

"Boys," he said earnestly, "you are bigger than anything that can ever happen to you. Always remember this."

"I don't want to be called puny," Lee insisted hotly. "I'm not puny."

"I understand how you feel," said Mr. de Forest sympathetically. He reached for the black leather Bible on his desk, but he didn't open it. Presently he laid it down again.

Finally he placed his right hand on Lee's shoulder and his left hand on Charles' shoulder and looked straight into the boys' eyes. "The real test comes in how you face up to problems," he said seriously. "Let me repeat. You are bigger than anything that can ever happen to you!"

"I want to be big and tall," Lee declared. "I want to be bigger than those boys."

"You will be," his father assured him. "Just don't forget you can be tall in spirit as well as tall in body."

91

UNIVERSITY SCHOOL LIBRARY, K. S. D.

446973

Lee's First Invention

LEE STEPPED into the washtub of hot water, close beside the kitchen stove to take his Saturday night bath. Every Saturday night each member of the de Forest family was supposed to take a bath.

First Lee scrubbed his body with the wash cloth lathered with white soap. Then he washed off the soap and curled up in the round tub to relax for a few minutes.

Finally he climbed out of the tub and wiped his skin dry with a towel. Afterwards he put on cotton flannel pajamas and ran to his father's study. As always Mr. de Forest greeted him warmly and asked him to sit by the fire. Sometimes he asked Lee questions about school or school work. At other times he gave Lee advice or comforted him if he seemed to be worried.

In a little while, Lee kissed his father and started up to bed. He hurried through the cold hallway and climbed the front stairs, hanging onto the polished railing for help. At the head of the stairs he came to the bedroom which he shared with his brother.

Charles was sound asleep on Lee's side of the bed, just as usual when he went to bed first. Lee tried to push Charles over, but Charles woke up and started to fight. Then the boys carried on a pillow fight in bed until they heard their father coming up the stairs, three steps at a time.

Quickly the boys tumbled into bed and hid under the covers before he could reach the room. They tried to pretend they were asleep, but they could not help giggling.

Lee had tried a number of plans to prevent Charles from using the wrong side of the bed, but none had been successful. Suddenly he thought of a simple invention that might solve his problem with Charles. He wondered why he had not thought of it before.

The simple invention which Lee thought of was a bedstick. He cut a long, narrow piece of black walnut wood the right length to place lengthwise in the bed. Then he carefully padded the ends with old rags which he obtained from his mother. Now the stick would not scratch the bedstead or tear holes in the sheet.

After Lee finished making the bedstick, he took it upstairs to the bedroom. He placed it in the bed and measured carefully to make the space on each side the same. He wanted to place the bedstick exactly in the center so that Charles would have the same space that he would. He wanted to be fair with Charles.

While he was working, he heard Charles coming up the stairs and hid behind the door. Charles did not notice the bedstick until he climbed into bed. Immediately he realized what Lee had done and began to laugh. Carefully he moved the bedstick over to Lee's side of the bed.

Lee ran from his hiding place and moved the stick back to the center of the bed. He tried to help Charles to see that he had half of the bed. From then on he had little trouble with Charles about room for sleeping.

Lee's mother was a skilled pianist and a singer with a well-trained soprano voice. Lee enjoyed hearing his mother sing, especially the songs in which she trilled like a bird.

Mr. de Forest had no knowledge of music, but he was proud of his wife's ability. Both parents were eager for their three children to learn to play the piano well.

Mary began to take music lessons shortly after

the de Forests arrived in Talladega. She became greatly interested in music and didn't mind practicing many hours a day. As a result, she became a fine musician.

Lee felt differently from Mary about taking music lessons. When his mother suggested that he study piano, he argued with her. "Men don't play the piano," he insisted.

"Some of the greatest musicians and composers in the world are men," Mrs. de Forest told him. "People everywhere greatly respect and admire these famous musicians."

"Only a sissy wants to learn to play," Lee said stubbornly. "I'd be ashamed to be seen playing a piano."

"You will regret that you don't understand music later on," his mother warned him.

Lee held out in his objection to taking piano lessons, but finally consented to learn to play the cornet. He felt that the piano was suitable

96

only for women to play, but that the cornet was suitable for men to play.

"Mama," Lee said one day to Mrs. de Forest, "if you insist that I become a musician, why don't you let me play the cornet?"

"I'll think about it and talk it over with your father," answered Mrs. de Forest.

Lee's parents finally decided that it was better to have a fairly good cornetist in the family than a poor pianist. A few days later Lee and his mother went downtown and purchased a second-hand cornet.

On the way home they stopped to see a blind musician, who lived along the way. This musician played the cornet and promised to give lessons to Lee every other week.

"I intend to practice every day and learn to play the cornet so well that you will be proud of me," Lee announced to his mother while they were walking home.

"I hope you do," she said, "now that you have chosen to play a cornet."

Lee kept his promise and practiced playing the cornet regularly. Sometimes he played it so loud that neighbors objected.

Soon after Lee began to take cornet lessons, Mr. de Forest bought a horse, which the children named Jenny Lind. The horse immediately became a family pet, and the children rode everywhere horseback. Lee even rode horseback to take lessons on his cornet.

Music was very popular in the college at Talladega. Several members of the faculty had fine, well-trained voices, and took a great interest in vocal music. They encouraged the students to sing and helped them to form both a glee club and a choir. Some of the singers had very unusual voices.

This glee club and choir specialized in singing beautiful old Negro spirituals. The haunting quality of these songs touched Lee, and he never tired of hearing them. Mrs. de Forest and the singing members of the faculty arranged many musical programs which were thoroughly enjoyed by the community and school.

Even though Lee had homework to do and his cornet to practice, he always found time to read the magazine, called *The Youth's Companion*. He was fascinated by the advertisement of miniature outfits for boys that could be ordered. One day he sent for a small silverplating outfit which was advertised.

When the set came, Lee examined it carefully and was eager to test it. He wanted to find out how well it would work. If it worked as well as he hoped it would, perhaps he could use it to earn extra money.

Lee obtained permission from his mother to test the outfit on the family knives, forks, and spoons, all of which were badly battered and worn. First he read the directions that had come with the outfit. Then he started to work on one of the spoons and could hardly wait to see what it would be like. He held it up and noticed that it looked almost like new.

Lee replated all the family silver, and his mother was delighted with the results of his work. "Why, Lee," she exclaimed, "my old worn silver looks like new. Now I'll be proud of it whenever I entertain people."

Mrs. de Forest's enthusiasm made Lee all the more eager to earn money by plating. His monthly allowance of ten cents was not nearly enough to pay for everything he wanted. Sometimes he made a few more cents by selling a half-dozen eggs, but he did not have an opportunity to sell eggs very often.

Now, if he could plate and replate the neighbor's silver, he could earn quite a bit of extra money. One afternoon after school he walked over to Mrs. Andrews' house and knocked on the front door. Soon Mrs. Andrews came to the door and said graciously, "Hello, Lee."

At first, Lee was tongue-tied and stood without answering. He had never asked people to let him do work before. Then he thought of the money that he wanted to earn. He needed the money to buy a special kind of saw that he had seen advertised. With this special kind of saw, he could make fancy designs, like scrolls.

"Mrs. Andrews," Lee began, "have you any old knives and forks that you would like to have look new and shiny again?"

"I most certainly have," she said.

"I have a new silver-plating outfit," Lee explained. He was not shy or tongue-tied now. "I've just plated my mother's knives and forks and spoons. She says they look as new as the day she bought them. Look at this." He showed Mrs. Andrews a spoon he had plated.

"The spoon looks new," said Mrs. Andrews.

Even with a new source of income, Lee could not earn money very fast. Before long, he saw an advertisement about something that he wanted to purchase even more than the saw.

The latest issue of *The Youth's Companion* featured a little upright steam engine with an alcohol boiler. Lee thought of all the fun he could have with a toy of this sort. He worked even harder to earn money.

After he had ordered the engine he waited impatiently for word from the express office. One day when it was raining, he suddenly felt sure that the engine had arrived. He had no notice from the express office, but put on his rubber boots and coat and started out. Then he sloshed through the mud and water to the office.

Leaving a trail of water behind him, he walked up to a clerk behind a wire cage. "Sir, have you a package for Lee de Forest?" he asked.

The man looked at the water-soaked boy. "Are you Lee de Forest?" he asked.

"Yes, sir, I am," Lee answered politely.

"Wait a minute," the clerk said. He looked at the labels on a number of boxes stacked here and there in the office. At last he picked up a box and came carrying it back to the wire cage. "Here's your package, son."

"Thank you," said Lee. He was so eager to see the little engine that he opened the box right in the express office.

The engine was all that he had hoped it would be. He placed it carefully under his raincoat and plowed through the mud and water back to the college to try it out.

As Lee watched the little engine run, he was the happiest boy in town. Most of all he enjoyed opening a valve and listening to the tiny whistle. He couldn't do this often, however, as it used up too much steam.

The engine was expensive to run, because it burned alcohol, which was very costly at that time. Lee soon found that he could burn ethyl to run the engine. This was much better because ethyl was cheaper than alcohol.

From the first, Mr. de Forest considered this

engine a great extravagance. One day he said to Lee, "Son, I won't allow you to waste your money or mine on this engine."

Lee couldn't think of anything to say, but was disappointed. He wondered whether he could use the kitchen stove for heat.

He took a can opener and cut away the part of the engine that held the alcohol. Then he set the boiler directly on the top of the stove. His idea worked. Now he could burn wood and coal to get steam.

"Lee," the cook objected, "you're always in the way when I have to get dinner."

"Please let me hear the whistle a few more times," Lee pleaded.

Gradually Lee became interested in other things and quit playing with his engine. The cook was delighted, because he stayed out of her way in the kitchen.

A Locomotive in the Back Yard

Soon Lee became interested in locomotives and how they traveled forward and backward. He read an article about locomotives in an encyclopedia in the college library. From this article he could understand fairly well how locomotives could move forward, but he couldn't understand how they could move backward.

One day on his way home from the iron works, he stopped at the railroad yard. There on a side track he found a big locomotive.

The locomotive had no fire in the firebox or steam in the boiler. Here was an opportunity to find out how an engineer reversed an engine.

Lee walked over to the locomotive and climbed up the steps into the cab. He sat down on the engineer's seat and imagined that he was running the engine. He tried to move the heavy reversing lever, but, of course, nothing happened. He wanted to know how it felt to make the great engine move forward and backward.

Soon he climbed down from the cab and crawled under the locomotive. Since there was no steam in the boiler, he knew that he would be safe. Lying with his back on the wooden ties, he examined the bottom of the boiler. He checked all the moving parts underneath.

He tried to figure out how each moving part worked. He studied the reversing mechanism from below until he was quite sure that he understood it. Then he crawled out and skipped along the path home.

"Oh, I'm happy, I'm so happy!" he sang. He had a project in mind. He would build a locomotive in the back yard. Already he could see how the locomotive would look.

"Charles," Lee called as he ran up the steps of the house, two at a time, "how would you like to help me build a locomotive?"

"Where can we build a locomotive?" inquired Charles, his eyes sparkling.

"Right here in the yard," said Lee.

"When can we start?" asked Charles.

"Let's start now," answered Lee.

A section under the house which Lee called "The Dark Place" was filled with pieces of wood which had been left over from building the house. Also, there were boxes, barrels, paint kegs, and oil cans which had been stored there.

The boys dragged out lumber and other things and placed them in the back yard. Then they sorted out things which they could use.

"Those barrel heads will make good wheels for the locomotive," Lee said to his brother.

Charles had carried one of them outside and was looking at it.

The boys worked hard on the locomotive and gradually put the different parts together. The last part which they put in place was the cowcatcher. Finally when the locomotive was nearly finished, they stood back a short distance to look at it and admire it.

"It looks good," said Charles.

"Yes, it looks all right," Lee said in agreement, "even the cowcatcher."

"So does the smokestack," said Charles.

The boys crawled into the cab, and Lee touched the throttle. "Chug-chug-chug," he began slowly. "Chug-a-chug-chug-chug." He spoke faster and faster as he imagined that the engine was picking up speed.

Lee had planned the locomotive carefully. He had even figured out a reversing lever which moved parts under the boiler. Of course, the locomotive wouldn't run, but he could shift the lever and imagine that he was making it move forward or backward. The boys also played with other parts which would move.

The locomotive still lacked a bell. The boys searched everywhere, but couldn't find one. Finally they asked their mother for help.

Mrs. de Forest shook her head. "There used to be a bell in your Grandfather Robbins' attic in Iowa," she said slowly. "If it is still there, we might get it for you."

Lee wanted the bell right now. He didn't want to wait long enough to write a letter to Iowa or have a bell sent from Iowa.

Maybe he could find a bell in Talladega. He hesitated to go into town because the town boys often teased him. They often called him names and acted as if they wanted to start a fight and make him fight, too.

"Being called names won't hurt me," he said

110

out loud. He wanted the bell so much that he was willing to put up with teasing, if need be. Possibly he wouldn't see the boys.

Lee really was not afraid of the boys, even though they were larger. He just wanted to avoid fighting them, yet he felt that he could win. Many times his father had reminded him that in the long run it was much better to avoid a fight than to have one.

Lee and Charles hunted in several stores and junk shops for a bell, but couldn't find one. Finally they were about ready to give up.

"Let's go home," urged Charles.

Lee looked down the street. "There's another junk shop down there somewhere," he said. "Let's look there first."

"All right," said Charles reluctantly.

When they walked into the store, they saw one of the town boys in another aisle. Charles tried to pull his brother toward the door.

"We won't find a bell here," Charles whispered to his brother. "Let's go home."

"We haven't even looked yet," said Lee.

The town boy in the aisle called out, "What are you looking for?"

Much to Lee's surprise, the boy seemed friendly and interested. Lee told the boy that they wanted to purchase a bell.

"Why do you want a bell?" the boy asked.

"For a locomotive that we have built at our house," Lee explained.

"Is the locomotive big enough to get in?" the town boy asked. He seemed to be more and more friendly and interested.

"Yes, would you like to go home with us to see it?" Lee asked generously.

"Maybe I would," the town boy said slowly. "Let me help you look for a bell."

"Fine," Lee said. He and Charles left the boy and started to look around.

A few minutes later the town boy called out, "Hey, come here. I've found a bell."

Lee and Charles hurried over. Sure enough! There was just the kind of bell that the boys needed to finish their locomotive.

Lee thanked the boy. Then he began to examine the bell more closely and noticed that it was cracked. His face fell.

"Maybe the storekeeper has another bell that isn't cracked," the boy suggested.

Just then the storekeeper, a short man with a black mustache, came over. Lee asked him whether he had another bell.

The man shook his head. "That's the only bell I have in the store," he said.

"How much is it?" Lee inquired.

"It's only a quarter."

Lee hadn't expected to get a bell for so little money, even a cracked bell. "I'll take it," he said, reaching for his money.

113

The town boy followed Charles and Lee outside. He watched them put the cracked bell into the cart and start for home.

"Thanks for finding the bell for us," Lee said. "I hope you'll come to see our locomotive when you can."

"I'll try to come," the town boy said.

The de Forest brothers were grateful to the town boy for helping them find the bell. When they reached home, they climbed up on the locomotive and put the bell in place. Lee tied a short rope to the bell that led to the cab. Now he could ring the bell from the cab just as engineers did on real locomotives.

"I'm the engineer and you're the fireman," Lee announced. "Check to be sure there's plenty of wood in the firebox. We need lots of steam to move the locomotive."

The next Saturday morning, Lee and Charles had visitors in their back yard. They were surprised to see several town boys come walking toward the locomotive.

Lee, who was in the cab, waved to them. "Hello," he called cheerfully.

"We came to see the locomotive," said the boy who had found the bell.

"See the bell?" said Charles pointing.

"How does it sound?" the boy asked.

Lee pulled hard on the rope. *Clang, clang.*

"It sounds all right," said the boy, looking at it rather proudly.

While the town boys were admiring the de Forest brothers' project, one of the Lewis boys wandered into the yard. His father was a prominent man in Talladega.

"Did you make the locomotive?" he asked.

Lee nodded. "Yes, Charles and I made it all by ourselves," he said proudly.

"I wish I could make a locomotive as good as this," he said enviously.

115

KENT STATE UNIVERSITY LIBRARY, KENT, OHIO

"Get in and take a ride," Lee suggested.

"Gee, I'd like to," the Lewis boy said. "I have chores to do at the farm this morning, but I'll be back later."

116

"The locomotive won't run, will it?" asked one of the town boys.

"No," answered Lee, "but we imagine that it does. It's fun to think that it does."

The guests stayed a long time and inspected the locomotive thoroughly. When they started to leave, Lee said, "Come again."

"We will," they answered.

"The town boys act like friends," said Charles. "We have made some new friends."

"I think we have, too," said Lee, starting to ring the bell louder than before.

As people in the town and neighborhood heard about the locomotive, many children and their parents came to see it. The parents usually gave the excuse that they came with their children. Lee showed the locomotive to all visitors, explained how it was made, and pointed out the different parts.

Even Mr. de Forest was impressed by what

Lee and Charles had accomplished. "I am proud of how resourceful you are," he said.

"At least I have found out how a reversing gear works," answered Lee.

One of the neighbors said to Mr. de Forest, "You must be very proud of Lee. I wish that my boy showed that kind of ability."

Mr. de Forest smiled. "Lee does seem to have a special knack for mechanical things," he said. He glanced at Lee, who was working the lever in the engineer's cab and explaining something to a boy from down the street.

"If he gets a chance," the neighbor continued, "some day he may become an inventor."

"We expect him to become a minister or a teacher," said Mr. de Forest, "but I'm glad to see him making friends."

The Blast Furnace

ONE YEAR a group of engineers from the North came to Talladega to build a blast furnace for smelting iron ore. Lee's curiosity was aroused, and he became intensely interested in the blast furnace and how it would work. Soon he spent all his free time watching the men work about a mile from the college.

If his mother wanted him, she sent Charles to summon him. He never tired of watching the mechanics rivet together the steel plates for the tanks. The loud noise seemed like music to his ears, and he wished that he could climb up and use one of the rivet machines himself.

The engineers built a little railroad to bring iron ore from the mine. Men would load the cars with iron ore in the mine, and an engine would pull it to the furnace.

He could hardly wait for the furnace and railroad to start working. "When will everything be ready?" he asked one of the engineers.

"We're working as fast as we can," the man replied. "This is a big undertaking, and we have to build everything right."

At last the blast furnace and railway were completed, and Lee watched all the operations carefully. He especially enjoyed casting time, when the workers, dripping with sweat, pulled a plug from the base of the huge furnace to let out the melted metal.

At blasting time a stream of yellow liquid or molten iron came roaring down the main sluices into hundreds of side molds. Then it would cool slowly and form pig iron.

Lee watched carefully and asked many questions, until he knew most of the details of how pig iron was made. He learned how and why ore, limestone, and coke were dumped into the furnaces. He understood how the gas ovens and the air compressors worked. He knew how to get ready for a casting, and how to draw off the slag at the top of the molten metal.

The men around the blast furnace seemed to enjoy having Lee spend time around the furnace. They called him "inquisitive lad" and freely answered his questions. Most of them were greatly impressed with his interest and his intelligent questions. They were willing to take time to answer him.

One day while Lee was watching the men work, he suddenly decided to build a blast furnace of his own. All the way home he scuffed his feet along the dirt road, thinking of plans to build his furnace.

First he needed to collect materials for building the furnace. He had to use whatever he could find, because he had no money for buying things. In the basement he found chunks of lead to use in place of iron ore.

Charles tagged after him. "What are you going to make?" he asked.

"A blast furnace," answered Lee.

"What's a blast furnace?" asked Charles.

"A blast furnace is a device for smelting ore," Lee answered.

Lee found an old ash can, which he could use as a furnace. He punched two holes near the bottom, one for forcing compressed air into the furnace and the other for letting hot molten metal flow out into a mold.

Beside his furnace he built a wooden frame to serve as an elevator shaft. On top of this wooden framework he fastened a strong, round crosspiece. Over the crosspiece he placed a long rope, one end of which was tied to the handle of an old pail in the shaft. By pulling on the rope, he could haul the pail full of fuel or other materials to the top of the furnace and dump it. Then he constructed a chimney of pine wood for the furnace.

He still had to have a supply of compressed air for the furnace. The bellows by the fireplace were exactly what he needed, so he made arrangements to borrow them. He fastened them to the lower part of the ash can.

Now he was ready to operate the furnace. He hauled a bucket of charcoal up the shaft and dumped it into the bottom of the furnace. He started a fire, and pumped the bellows lustily until the charcoal glowed red hot. Then he dumped chunks of limestone and lead on top of the glowing coals. Black smoke poured from the chimney of the furnace.

Lee tried putting different amounts of charcoal, limestone, and lead into the furnace. After many experiments, he found just the right mixture of material to use.

Finally one day, a small amount of melted lead trickled from the hole near the bottom of his furnace. The molten lead dripped into the

mold he had prepared in the sand bed. The blast furnace was a success.

Lee was delighted. He had worked many hours, but the result was worth his time and trouble. After this he made many other molds.

As Lee had anticipated, he had problems. Several times he burned his fingers and singed his hair and eyebrows. The wooden chimney caught on fire, and the nozzle burned off the bellows.

Both of Lee's parents were impressed with his resourcefulness. After he burned his hands, however, they wouldn't let him fire the furnace again. They decided that the furnace was too dangerous to use.

By now Lee had accomplished his purpose. He had wanted to build a blast furnace that would work, and he had done so. Soon he became interested in several other experiments.

Mechanical Drawings and Books

Mr. and Mrs. de Forest had little money, but they had many interests which they shared with their children. Mrs. de Forest, a talented and trained musician, arranged for all the children to take music lessons. She took them to musical programs at the college, where they could listen to good music.

The de Forest children always had a supply of good books to read. They had access to books in their home library and in the larger college library. They frequently received carefully chosen books as gifts, and both their parents often read to them.

The children always had work to do, but they were allowed to wander through the hills and woods around Talladega. They swam and fished in the river, learned about nature, and enjoyed the beauty of their surroundings.

At the age of twelve Lee was an active, fast-growing boy. He liked to go to school, and he studied hard, both at school and at home. He had a long list of regular chores to do at home, but he found time to read a great many books. He spent many hours reading at home and in the college library.

As Lee used the library more and more, he discovered that it contained publications, besides ordinary books. One of his favorites was the *Patent Office Gazette.*

The college librarian was intrigued by Lee, because he often read books which many adults couldn't understand. When she brought him the big oversized *Patent Office Gazette,* he always

127

turned immediately to the intricate drawings of machines. He studied these drawings with great interest, until he was quite sure he understood how the machines worked.

Lee not only studied the drawings in the big book, but he made drawings of his own. He copied the drawings of his favorite inventions and stored them in a large pasteboard box. His mother had once used the large box for storing patterns which she used in sewing.

At one time he became especially interested in steam hammers. He had first learned about steam hammers by reading about them in his father's encyclopedia. Now he studied their working parts as carefully as he had once studied the parts of steam locomotives.

He made detailed drawings of various kinds and sizes of steam hammers. He sketched on paper the pistons and steam valves that controlled the action of the hammers.

Usually he stretched out on the floor of the sitting room to work on his drawings. He spread a large sheet of paper on the floor and measured and drew lines in all directions. Moving here and there on the floor, he often worked for hours on a single drawing.

One day when he was absorbed in making a special drawing, a neighbor woman came to visit his mother. The woman looked curiously at the odd-looking mechanism which he was drawing, and wondered what it was.

"Does Lee know what he is drawing?" the woman asked in a low voice.

Mrs. de Forest smiled. "Oh, yes," she said proudly. "He understands subjects very thoroughly and he knows exactly what he is drawing. He is always eager to invent something."

On Saturday afternoons, Lee liked to go into the woods and imagine that he was a frontiersman or an Indian. He wandered far from the regular paths and blazed his own trail through unfamiliar territory.

Often in his travels, he rested under the shade of a tall tree. He sat listening to the wind and looking at the white clouds in the blue sky above. He studied the bark and leaves of the trees and the different kinds of flowering plants that grew in the woods. Sometimes he sat very still and watched small animals run here and there, unaware of his presence.

His mother often told him that his French ancestors must have lived in the forest and loved it as much as he did. The family name, de Forest, meant "of the forest."

Lee was a great student of the Bible and read it from cover to cover. He was especially fond of the story of Joseph.

He read many times how Joseph's brothers, because they were extremely jealous of him, sold him into slavery in Egypt. In this foreign country Joseph did his work so well as a slave that the ruler of Egypt made him a governor.

When Joseph's brothers faced a famine in their homeland, they went to Egypt to buy food. Joseph not only gave them food, but he finally arranged for them to come with his father and families to make their homes there. He gave them land and protected and cared for them in every way possible.

Twelve-year-old Lee wrote in his notebook that the story of Joseph made him realize that nothing good was accomplished without hard work. He was certain that a person may gain fame and wealth by hard labor and by doing right.

Perpetual Motion Machine

As LEE continued to read and study his father's books, he became interested in attempting to invent a perpetual motion machine or machine that would keep running forever. He read that for centuries scientists and inventors had tried to devise a machine of this kind, but that none had ever succeeded.

The books explained that a perpetual motion machine couldn't be made, because friction would wear out the parts. Lee wasn't satisfied with this explanation and carefully checked the sketches of machines that had been tried. He duplicated some of the drawings.

The more Lee worked with the drawings, the more interested he became. He studied every drawing in great detail.

He read article after article about perpetual motion in the college library. Most of the writers stated that it was impossible to invent a perpetual motion machine. On the other hand, many scientists and inventors had believed that it was possible, and had actually tried to invent a machine. Men had been trying to solve this problem for hundreds of years.

Lee thought and thought about the matter. He reasoned that if a machine could be made to operate for a long time, one could be made to operate forever. He would prove that it could be done, even though many said that it couldn't. He was determined to try.

Having decided, Lee was filled with excitement. He would invent a machine to supply all the power the world would ever need without cost. It would release millions of people from drudgery. Ideas began to form in his mind. He grabbed a sketch pad and began to draw.

He thought faster than he could insert his ideas in a drawing. He erased, revised, and threw away one sketch after another. Each time he added a few new features.

During most of his working hours for several weeks, he thought about his project. He spent all the time he could spare making detailed drawings of his wonderful machine.

Finally he completed the drawings of a machine that he felt certain would run forever. He was so certain that he imagined he could see the machine in operation. He was certain that he had succeeded where many others had failed. At thirteen, he thought triumphantly, he had invented a perpetual motion machine!

Of course, Lee was doomed to great disappointment. His perpetual motion machine, like those which had been made before, wouldn't keep on running. Obviously he couldn't understand why, because he thought that he had overcome all the mistakes of the former inventors.

Lee's long hours of thought and work had not been wasted. They had helped him to realize that he wanted to become an inventor. From now on he would study the right subjects to help him prepare for this kind of work. He liked science and felt that it offered many opportunities. He was confident that he could find answers to many important scientific questions later on in life.

At this time in 1886, Lee was interested in mechanical projects rather than electrical projects. Very little was known about electricity, and he had little opportunity to study the subject at Talladega.

Unlike boys today, Lee lacked experimental toys and equipment to help him carry on projects. He even lacked up-to-date copies of magazines and books. Most of those which he obtained from the college library were out-of-date. They failed to give him the latest information about discoveries and inventions.

Lee was very observing of things around him and was filled with curiosity. If no one could tell him what he wanted to know, he sought the answers through his own investigations. His lack of tools and up-to-date reading materials forced him to be resourceful.

Instead of going to a store or buying tools, he had to make many tools of his own. He had to use old pieces of metal and wood for materials to work with. Having to do things for himself caused him to work all the harder to succeed. He learned never to give up, and this training was of great value to him later on, after he became an inventor.

As Lee grew older he became eager to develop

physically and finally decided to build a gymnasium. He looked around the de Forest home for a suitable place to build it.

He thought first of the barn loft, but it was filled with hay. The only vacant place he could find was part of the cellar under the house. This cellar was hardly suited for a gymnasium, because it had a dirt floor and the ceiling was only seven feet high. He had no other place to use, however, so he set to work.

First he set up a trapeze in the cellar. When he hung from his knees, his head came almost to the ground and he could touch the ground with his hands. He decided that there must be more room for using the trapeze safely.

He couldn't make the ceiling any higher, so he obtained a shovel and dug a trench in the ground below the trapeze. Then he could swing on the trapeze, without danger of his head hitting the ground.

138

Lee and his brother Charles had fun exercising and performing stunts in the gymnasium, but they needed more equipment. They found strips of wood suitable for making parallel bars, except that the wood was rough. They covered the bars with rags and burlap.

One day Lee went to see the blacksmith at the college. While there he told the blacksmith about the gymnasium. "Building a gymnasium is a very good idea," said the blacksmith. "What can I do to help you?"

"We need some iron rings," answered Lee.

The blacksmith welded two iron rings of just the right size. The boys suspended the rings on strong ropes from beams in the ceiling. Then they could wind up the ropes, climb into the rings, and whirl round and round. Now the gymnasium was complete with equipment.

Lee and Charles and their friends spent many hours exercising in the gymnasium. At last

Charles became so tall that he could hardly use the trapeze and bars without hitting his head on the floor or ceiling.

About this time a professor at the college built a barn back of his house. The dramatic teachers at the school had been wanting to start a young people's theater. They decided that the loft of the new barn would make an ideal place for the theater.

The dramatic teachers chose first to produce a play about kings and knights and ladies. Lee was eager to be in this play. He remembered how much fun he and Mary and Charles had playing in their homemade castle.

At last Lee was chosen to play the part of a knight. His mother made him a doublet, or kind of close-fitting jacket, to wear.

"During the Middle Ages, when knights and ladies lived in Western Europe, many of the knights wore doublets," she explained.

Lee looked at the costume, but was not very happy about it. He put on the doublet and other pieces, but nothing seemed to fit. When he looked in the mirror of the big mahogany dresser, he hardly recognized himself.

"It's a beautiful costume," said his mother.

Lee looked questioningly at the embroidered doublet, the hat with the trailing feather, the long red stockings, and the green slippers. He pushed back the floppy ostrich plume on his beret which tickled his face.

The red stockings were much too long for his legs. The bright green slippers were too big for his feet. He raised one foot and wiggled it. The slipper fell off.

"You look like a noble knight," his mother said approvingly.

"I can't walk in these slippers," said Lee. "The slippers are too big for me."

"We'll stuff paper in the slippers to make them fit better, and then you can walk," said Mrs. de Forest assuringly.

Lee tried walking again and the slippers stayed on his feet. He still didn't like the costume, but he would get to carry a spear. It

142

would be worth wearing the costume just to get to carry the spear.

When the play was given, Lee played his part well. He was applauded by everyone in the audience. Now he was happy and agreed to take a part in the next play that was given.

His happiness soon disappeared, because he didn't like the part assigned to him in the next play. He was asked to be the wolf in "Little Red Riding Hood."

At the first rehearsal, he had to wrap himself in a sheepskin rug, obtained from a neighbor's parlor. He was supposed to crawl onto the stage on all fours and growl fiercely.

Lee's sister Mary, wearing a nightcap and spectacles, took the part of Granny, the helpless grandmother in the play. Lee was supposed to devour her, and this act made the whole play seem ridiculous.

As practice continued, Lee became more and

more dissatisfied with his part. He dragged himself to each practice period, largely because nobody was available to take his place.

The night the play was to be given, teachers and parents gathered to watch the play. Lee peeked out from behind the curtain and saw the different persons who had come. All at once he felt that he just couldn't go on.

His trouble wasn't fear. He simply didn't want to take the part of a wolf wearing a sheepskin. He didn't want to be laughed at for crawling on his hands and knees. When the time came, he stayed back of the curtain.

"You are holding up the play," the coach whispered. "Go on to the stage."

"I don't want to," Lee said stubbornly. He could see Grandmother on the stage. She was waiting for the wolf to appear.

The audience became restless. People began to wonder what was going on.

Suddenly Mary stepped to the front of the stage. "Mama," she called out, "Lee won't act his part. He's spoiling the play. Please come back stage and talk with him."

Mrs. de Forest left her seat and hurried backstage. "Lee," she said firmly, "you have the most interesting part in the play. Go out on the stage and start acting."

"I'll feel silly acting the part of a wolf," Lee tried to explain.

"It's an important part," Mrs. de Forest reminded him. It's the climax."

Lee crawled out on the stage. The people in the audience hadn't expected to see a wolf in sheep's clothing. They laughed and clapped. The play was more successful than the producers had expected. Lee was thankful, but never wanted to take the part of a wolf again.

Becoming an Inventor

MR. AND MRS. DE FOREST often talked about the de Forest scholarship at Yale College. A distant relative had given a large amount of money to the college so that members of the de Forest family could be educated there.

The scholarship had enabled Mr. de Forest to study at Yale. He expected Lee and Charles to use the scholarship in preparing to become ministers or teachers, and he saw that they studied the subjects required for entrance.

Both boys liked to listen to their father's stories of the delightful years he had spent studying at Yale.

146

Mr. de Forest was a Latin scholar, and he arranged for Lee to study this language in school. He even tutored Lee in Latin, and both father and son enjoyed the time they spent reading Latin selections together.

After Lee obtained a good start in Latin, Mr. de Forest arranged for him to study Greek. "You will need a thorough knowledge of Greek, not only to enter Yale, but to study sources of the Bible," he said. "You'll need it after you become a preacher."

By this time Lee knew that he wanted to become an inventor, and he was disturbed whenever his father mentioned his becoming a preacher. He wanted to study science and become an inventor in mechanical engineering. He didn't want to disappoint his father, but felt that he wouldn't become a good preacher.

One day he came across a bulletin from Yale's Sheffield Scientific School. He studied the bul-

letin and became convinced that this school—
rather than Yale College—was where he belonged. Eagerly he read descriptions of the
courses and the entrance requirements.

He found that Latin was required, so he began
to study Latin harder than ever. Greek was not
required, except the alphabet—which he had
already learned in his course in school.

Lee wondered how he could convince his
father that he should go to a scientific school,
rather than to Yale College. He knew that there
was no use to attempt to argue the matter. He
had argued unsuccessfully many times.

In the spring of 1889 when Lee was sixteen
years of age, he felt that he should begin his
career. He should make plans for the future by
preparing himself for his career.

Suddenly he thought of a new way to ap-
proach his father. He would put his thoughts in
a letter rather than attempt to express them

orally again. Often he was awed by his father's arguments and stern discipline.

He decided to type his letter and sat down to an old typewriter to work it out. He spent a long time composing and typing the letter.

He stated that he wanted to be a mechanic and inventor, because he thought he had great talents in that direction. Then he asked his father to let him prepare for such a career. He could prepare best, he explained, by attending Yale Sheffield Scientific School rather than Yale College.

Lee also reminded his father that he could prepare for the course in a shorter time than he could prepare for Yale College. This would be of great advantage to Mr. de Forest, who had three children to educate.

Finally Lee explained that he could obtain a good education at the scientific school. He would learn many of the same things as he would learn at Yale College, things in which his father was interested. He ended the letter, "Your obedient son," and signed his name.

Lee wondered what his father would think about the letter. He felt that his mother would understand how he felt. She had often said she wanted him to be happy and contented with his work. He turned the letter over and wrote on the back of it one of his favorite poems.

> Lives of great men all remind us
> We can make our lives sublime,
> And departing leave behind us
> Footprints on the sands of time.

Then he wrote, "Dear Mama: The only footprints I will leave will be my inventions. I should take the scientific course."

Mr. de Forest read the letter and called Lee into his study. Lee stood straight and tall before his father, but his stomach seemed to be filled with butterflies.

"Well, son," said Mr. de Forest calmly, "if you positively want this sort of half-baked education, you may have it."

He went on to say that Lee would miss all the pleasure of studying great books. He would not be allowed to live in the Yale dormitory, which his father remembered with great pleasure. He would not get to make friends with the best young men on the campus, as his father had. He wanted Lee to understand.

"I can only say I hope you never regret the choice you are now making," Mr. de Forest said at the end of his talk.

"I know I won't," Lee said positively.

From this time on Lee seemed to understand his father's many fine qualities. He realized how hard his father had worked to improve conditions at Talladega College.

Mr. de Forest had never spared himself in his efforts to raise money for new buildings or to secure the best teachers he could find. He did everything possible to help the students.

Through the years, Lee developed great admiration for Thomas A. Edison, the inventor. He remembered seeing and hearing Mr. Edison's talking machine when he was a small boy. Since that time he had acquired a biography about Edison, which he had read many times.

In the summer of 1891, when Lee was nineteen years old, he wrote Mr. Edison a letter. He asked Mr. Edison what preparation he should make to become an inventor. Then he waited eagerly for an answer from the famous inventor, but no answer ever came.

During these years Lee was very restless. He knew that he would be allowed to go to a scientific school, but wasn't certain when he could start. He still had to take preparatory courses before he could enter Sheffield Scientific School, courses not given at Talladega.

152

Mr. de Forest lacked money to send Lee away to school. He already was sending Mary to a girls' school in Massachusetts, and he couldn't afford to spend more at this time.

Lee was almost frantic about not being able to take the courses at Talladega that he needed for entrance at Sheffield Scientific School. To occupy his time, he tried to carry on experiments, some of which were successful and others unsuccessful.

Most of all Lee was interested in electricity. He read carefully about Mr. Edison's inventions and experiments, and tried to construct several electrical devices of his own.

All the experiments failed, and Lee realized that he needed to know more and to have better equipment. He realized that he could obtain neither more knowledge nor better equipment while he remained at Talladega.

In the spring of 1891, Lee decided to write

letters to companies, applying for work during the summer. He wrote letters to a number of companies in the North, where he hoped to be able to spend the summer.

Most of the letters went to companies that manufactured different kinds of equipment. Lee felt that he could learn many things in a factory that would help him in his scientific studies. However, he received few answers, and not a single offer of employment.

When the school year ended, Lee felt a strong sense of relief. After his last examination, he went home, read for a while, and practiced "Swanee River" on his cornet. He was to play this piece at the commencement exercises.

After Lee failed to find work for the summer, Mr. de Forest arranged for him to stay at a camp in Massachusetts. From there he was to go to Mt. Hermon Boys' School, which was located only about four miles from the school Mary was attending. At last he was to complete his preparation for Yale.

Before Lee left for the North, he went around the neighborhood to say good-by to his friends. First he went to Professor Andrews' house, where he had often gone to get a drink of cold water from the well.

"Good luck," Professor Andrews said, patting Lee on the shoulder.

"Thank you, sir," Lee answered, bowing politely before the old gray-haired professor. Mr. Andrews had taken a special interest in Lee, almost as if the lad were his son.

Lee stopped at Elisha Jones' home. Elisha was his best friend, and the person, outside the members of his family, that he would miss most of all. Elisha was planning to go away to college, too, when he could. He wanted to prepare to become a doctor.

Elisha ran out to meet Lee. "Hello," he said

awkwardly. "I guess we're about ready to bid each other good-bye. I'm getting packed, and wish we were going to the same school."

"You'll make a fine doctor," Lee said.

"You'll make a great inventor," Elisha said, "and be famous some day."

Lee dug the toe of his shoe in the loose soil, wondering what he should say in return. "Well, I plan to study hard, and do the best I can. I hope to be successful."

"You will be," Elisha said proudly, "just as someday I hope to be a good doctor."

Both boys realized their dreams. Elisha returned to Talladega, where he practiced medicine successfully for many years. Lee worked out hundreds of inventions.

At the summer camp, Lee took part in several sports. He learned to row and to swim well, and he practiced cross-country running.

Classes in electricity were offered at the camp,

which Lee found especially interesting. There was a small shop where he had an opportunity to carry on electrical experiments. He obtained enough electrical apparatus to build several electrical devices which he had not been able to make in Talladega.

In September Mr. de Forest came to help Lee enroll at the Mt. Hermon Boys' School. Lee was greatly impressed with the students, all of whom seemed bigger and more confident than he was. He felt very timid around the boys and wondered whether or not he belonged there.

Lee had to take entrance examinations in several subjects and felt gratified with his grades. He did exceptionally well in Latin, which pleased both him and his father.

Lee had certain disappointments at the school. He was disappointed because he had to help with the farm work. He felt that he was wasting time that he should be spending on his studies.

He was disappointed because the school offered no courses in science. One of the teachers, however, was interested in science and encouraged Lee to go on with his investigation. The two often discussed scientific projects, and the teacher furnished a number of books on science for Lee to read and study.

The boys were seldom allowed to leave the campus of the school. They spent all their time studying lessons or milking cows, digging potatoes, picking apples, or carrying on other work on the school farm.

On Sunday the students, including Lee, walked four miles to church. They walked this distance to hear Dwight L. Moody, a famous preacher of the time. Also on Sunday Lee often walked several miles away to visit his sister Mary, who still was enrolled at the seminary, or girls' school. Lee and Mary greatly enjoyed seeing each other frequently.

Occasionally some of the girls from Mary's school were invited to come to Mt. Herman for an evening entertainment. Whenever they were expected, the boys became greatly excited and made special preparation for the event.

The boys bathed, put on their best clothes and slicked their hair. There was great confusion, because the bathtubs were scarce, and each boy had a fixed time of fifteen minutes for taking a bath.

The de Forests could not afford to let Mary and Lee come home for Christmas. The train fare from Massachusetts to Alabama and back was far more than they could afford to spend. During the holidays, however, Lee had an exciting experience. He talked on the telephone for the first time.

There were very few telephones in 1891. Alexander Graham Bell had invented the telephone in 1876, but at first people could only talk for

159

short distances. By now, however, a few long-distance telephone lines had been built.

In 1881, a line had been built between Boston and Providence, Rhode Island—a distance of 45 miles. In 1884, a long-distance line was opened between Boston and New York—a distance of 292 miles. After that, a few other lines had been constructed between large cities.

Lee had been especially interested in telephones, because Thomas A. Edison had invented certain telephone improvements. He had seen few telephones and certainly had not expected to have the opportunity to talk over one.

One of the professors had arranged for Lee to talk by telephone with Mary at the seminary. The professor worked and worked to get a connection with the seminary, and finally reached Mary at the other end of the line.

"Hello, Mary," Lee shouted excitedly. "Do you know who this is? How are you? I'll bet you're surprised to have me call you over the telephone. Have you heard from Mama and Papa?"

The connection was poor and the only response Lee received was a loud buzzing sound. He tried to talk again, but the loud buzzing sound continued.

Lee was bitterly disappointed, and finally hung up in despair. He found out later that Mary could not understand him, either. He was ashamed to tell the professor that he couldn't talk with Mary.

He thanked the kind professor and went out into the cold, gray winter again. The homesickness, which he had been trying to fight, came back in full force. He had never before been away from home during the Christmas holidays.

"I'm disappointed in Edison," he muttered as he waded through snow back to the cheerless dormitory. "Somebody ought to be able to make telephones better than that."

Studies, examinations, winter chores, and before long, spring planting kept the boys busy for the next few months. All at once Lee and his roommate realized that the school year would soon be over. Both of them wanted to get jobs to earn money during the summer.

The boys tried to get work in the shops and stores and on the farms, but there seemed to be a dozen applicants for every job. Money was scarce, and few places were interested.

In desperation the boys grabbed an opportunity to become book agents, selling copies of King's *Handbook of the United States* from door to door. With a number of other hopeful book agents, they were trained for ten days. Then each boy set out, carrying a copy of the large, heavy volume under his arm.

Lee soon found out that people in New England weren't much interested in buying the book. He tried hard, but during the first two days he sold two books. In each case he lowered the price of the book so much that he made only a few cents profit.

Lee was determined and kept on working. He walked so far each day that by night he was completely exhausted. His feet burned and he was always hungry, because he had little to eat. He sold a few books, however, and by fall, he had forty dollars in his pocket to help pay for his last year at preparatory school.

During the fall term a new science hall was built at Mt. Hermon. At last Lee had a chance to take courses in science. Also he obtained a job cleaning one of the laboratories.

At the end of the year, Lee ranked first among all the students in science. He was chosen to give the scientific oration at the class exercises and talked on his favorite subject, "Scientific Discovery."

After the graduation exercises, he plunged

immediately into study for the entrance examinations at Yale Sheffield, studying ten hours a day. When he took the examinations at New Haven, Connecticut, about ten days later, he passed successfully. The de Forest scholarship would pay his tuition.

That summer Lee had hoped to work at the World's Columbian Exposition, which was being held in Chicago. He had applied for a position as a guide, but finally received a letter, saying that no positions would be available.

Lee was disappointed. He decided to sell enough books to earn money to go to Chicago anyway. Day after day he dragged on selling two or three books. Finally he accumulated eighteen dollars—the price of a round-trip ticket to Chicago. He went to the railroad station, bought a ticket, and boarded a train for the fair.

When Lee reached the fairgrounds, he headed for Machinery Hall. He spent all day studying typewriters, locomotives, farm machinery, and other machines. He was amazed at what the inventors had accomplished and wished that he could stay there all summer.

While he was looking at an engine, trying to figure out how it worked, he overheard someone say that there was a shortage of chair-pushers at the fair. He immediately went out, asked for a job, and was hired. Now he could stay at the fair until it was time to go to Yale.

The chairs were mounted on wheels, so that they could be pushed about. Many visitors rented the push-chairs to save walking about over the dusty grounds.

Whenever patrons asked Lee to recommend good exhibits to see, he always suggested Machinery Hall. Then he pointed out different machines and explained how they worked.

One man exclaimed, "I've never understood machinery, but you have explained it simply."

Hungry for Knowledge

LEE FOUND Yale strange and beautiful. He loved the streets lined with elm trees, the fine old brick or white wooden houses, and the spacious, well-kept lawns. He loved the wide sweep of the campus, with its impressive buildings, shaded lawns, and pleasant walks.

He found a room where he could study as late as he wished. He was hungry for knowledge, and didn't want someone telling him to quit studying and go to bed.

He had to be very careful about spending money, because he had little to spend. Fortunately he found a restaurant, where he could get nourishing meals for fifteen cents apiece. At times he bought a ticket at the restaurant, which allowed him to eat three meals a day for a week, at a slight saving.

Lee studied hard to prepare his lessons, but he found time to go to football games and to attend lectures which were not connected with his classes. Here he found a rich new life—filled with science, books, and friends.

His greatest problem was to pay for his room and board. He received a letter from his parents saying that they could not afford to help him. In desperation he took a job, working for a graduate student at ten cents an hour. Finally he found that he needed to earn more, so he obtained a position in a restaurant, where he waited on tables for his meals.

Every hour seemed to be filled with work or study, yet he found time to become interested in telegraphy. He learned telegraphy by studying books in the library, and thought that he might make telegraphy his future work.

He still yearned to become an inventor and could scarcely wait to invent something. One day he happened to see an announcement, offering $50,000 for submitting the best design for an underground trolley system.

During the next few weeks Lee read widely and completed a design. He sent it off with high hopes and felt certain that he would win the prize. After a long time the designs were returned with a notation that the original offer had been withdrawn.

Lee worked on other inventions—a game, a bar for a typewriter, and a joint for a compass. Not one of them was accepted.

At the end of Lee's first year at Yale, he obtained very good grades and received honorable mention in chemistry. He was doubly pleased at this recognition, because his father came unexpectedly to join him in the end-of-the-year festivities at Yale.

During the summer he lived in a room at the home of one of the professors. He mowed and watered the professor's lawn to pay for his room. He also worked all day in one of the college laboratories.

Often he rose at four o'clock in the morning to look after the lawn before he started to the laboratory. By night, after eight hours in the laboratory, he was too tired to study or think. He was even too weary to make drawings or models of inventions.

When school began in the fall, Lee moved back to his old room. He won honors in French, German, and English, and greatly enjoyed his courses in mechanical engineering.

Again he had to work hard to pay his way, and the money he earned was never enough for his needs. He ate the cheapest food he could find,

and frequently had no food at all. Despite this continued hardship, he kept studying far into the night.

One evening Lee went skating with friends, wearing clothes unsuited to the icy New England winter. He came home, wet and cold, and the next morning was seriously ill with chills and a fever. The college doctor came to see him and sent him to the Yale Infirmary.

Lee soon began to feel better and developed a ravenous appetite. He was especially pleased, because he could have all the food he wanted to eat without paying for it. He was sorry when he was well enough to leave, because it meant returning to his old way of living.

After Lee returned to school, he regained his strength very slowly. He found it more difficult to study and his subjects seemed harder than before. He lost interest in his work and found himself falling asleep when he should have been working. One day an instructor called him lazy, and he was inclined to agree with the instructor. Gradually, however, through weeks and months, he renewed his interest and ambition.

About this time he began reading about the accomplishments of Nikola Tesla, a brilliant electrical engineer in Europe. He was greatly interested in what this young genius was discovering about high-tension and high-frequency electrical currents. He wrote in his diary that he hoped to equal and excel Tesla.

During the year, he entered a number of contests, hoping to earn money. He wrote a number of stories and essays, but failed to win any prizes. He tried to invent a telephone relay, but it attracted little attention. All in all, his second year at Yale Sheffield proved to be discouraging to the young scientist.

When school was over for the year, he obtained a position as a waiter in a hotel on an island off the coast of New England. He spent a very restless, unpleasant summer at this hotel with only thirty dollars to show for his work.

Before school began, Lee had a delightful visit with his parents. Mr. and Mrs. de Forest came north and rented a house in a quiet Connecticut valley. While they were here, Lee and his father took long walks together, and found that they had many things to talk about. These visits were fortunate, because they were the last that Lee ever had with his father. Early the next year Mr. de Forest died.

The third year at Yale Sheffield would be Lee's last year, because the scientific course included three years. Lee wondered how he was going to support himself during his last year. He had hoped to earn a little money by having a story published in a magazine. Soon after school started, however, the manuscript was returned and coldly rejected.

174

After Lee's father died, Lee had to economize more than ever. He worked for his board in a restaurant and earned an extra dollar a week. He was granted a scholarship, which he could keep as long as his grades were high.

Lee still wanted to study hard and to learn, but by now he began to look forward to graduation. He felt that he had done excellent work in certain courses, but neither professors nor students were particularly impressed with his accomplishments.

There was a chapter of Sigma Xi, a scientific honor society, at Yale. Lee hoped to be elected to membership in the society, even though he had low marks in one course.

He thought that the society might find merit in some of the scientific articles he had written. Also he thought that the society might be impressed with the fact that he wanted to become a scientist. His hopes were futile.

Lee was disappointed, but he still had confidence. "I will honor them, and not they me," he wrote in his diary. Thirty-three years later, after he had become a famous inventor, he became an honorary member of Sigma Xi.

In 1896, when Lee graduated, scientists were excited over Professor Roentgen's discovery of X-rays. Lee's excitement over this discovery made him more certain than ever that he wanted to become a scientist and an inventor.

Lee realized that he still had much to learn and decided to take graduate work at Yale. He didn't know how he could pay his way, but he felt that he needed all the knowledge he could get. He needed knowledge in order to make important inventions.

At commencement time, while he was dreaming of a great future, his classmates voted him the nerviest and homliest member of the class!

Mystery Waves
and Electronics

LATER the following spring Mrs. de Forest
decided to move to New Haven. Mary, who
now was an accomplished pianist, would give
lessons to help support the family. Lee would
work to earn money and attend graduate school
at Yale. Charles would complete work for enter-
ing Yale the next year.

Lee found a large house, where the four de
Forests could live and where they could rent
rooms to students. Mrs. de Forest arrived about
the time Lee graduated.

During the summer Lee searched for work in
New Haven and the surrounding area, but jobs

were scarce and he could find nothing to do. He spent much of the time inventing a chainless bicycle and reading books.

Lee submitted his chainless bicycle invention to a bicycle company, but it was rejected. Fortunately, his father had left a few thousand dollars, so the family was not destitute. Besides, Mary earned small sums by giving piano lessons in the neighborhood.

Lee was relieved when the summer vacation ended, and he could begin graduate studies. He devoted most of his time to laboratory work, where he experimented with electric generators. At last he was taking electrical engineering, which he had long waited for.

An outstanding professor of mathematics stimulated Lee and encouraged him to continue his graduate studies a second year. By now Lee was involved in several investigations, which he wished to continue. He was especially interested in light waves and electronics. At that time very little was known about electronics, and he hoped to have an opportunity to study the subject thoroughly.

With the help of two professors, Lee set up a laboratory in the basement of a building on the campus. He wanted to measure wave lengths and frequencies in his study of electronics.

One night when Lee was working with a battery in his basement laboratory, an important person was delivering a lecture in the room above. In the midst of the talk, Lee's experiment caused a fuse to blow, and the lights went out. The audience had to leave by candle light before hearing the end of the lecture.

A professor was furiously angry with Lee about the blown fuse. He also accused Lee of pounding nails in a laboratory table. He told Lee that a man with no more sense than to do these things would never amount to anything.

The professor insisted that Lee should leave Sheffield, but the others who had been favorably impressed by his work intervened. Fortunately he was allowed to try for a Ph.D. over the objections of the angry professor.

In April, 1898, when Lee was absorbed in his experiments, the United States declared war on Spain. Like most Americans, Lee was interested in freeing Cuba from Spanish rule.

He decided to leave school temporarily and volunteered to join the United States Army. He drilled for several weeks at an army camp and finally became a bugler. Now he was pleased that he had learned to play the cornet.

The war was soon over. In September Lee returned to New Haven, healthier and stronger, and glad to go on with his studies. Furthermore, he had earned a little money.

Lee studied, listened to increasingly difficult lectures, and carried on his research work with new enthusiasm. Soon he was allowed to begin work on his thesis, which was required for graduation. The subject of this thesis was "Reflection of Hertzian Waves from the Ends of Parallel Wires."

Lee chose this subject, because he was particularly interested in the work of Dr. Heinrich Hertz, a German physicist, who had discovered electromagnetic, or radio, waves some ten years before. These waves were called Hertzian waves, because Dr. Hertz had discovered them. Lee realized that these waves carried many possibilities in the field of communication.

For seven months Lee worked hard and long to complete his thesis. In addition, he had to study and review for gruelling final examinations, which lasted for three days. His thesis was accepted and he passed his examinations, after which he was allowed to graduate. Then he became Dr. Lee de Forest.

Father of Radio

AFTER A short vacation, Dr. Lee de Forest, who was now twenty-five years old, went to Chicago to find work. He found employment in the telephone laboratory of an electric company at $10.00 a week. In a short time he was transferred to work on telephone cables, and from there to an experimental laboratory.

Telephone communication had greatly improved during the years when de Forest was completing his education. The telephone industry had become prosperous, because telephones were coming into wide use. They now were being used by homes and places of business in most parts of the country. De Forest was happy to be associated with this kind of industry.

Soon de Forest began to carry on experiments in a corner of the laboratory where he worked. He spent his lunch hour and an hour after work in the evening on these experiments. He was particularly interested in wireless communication or transmitting sound without wires.

At this time only a few scientists were interested in wireless communication. Lee worked hard to find a way to transmit sound over longer distances. He tried making devices of different materials, but none would transmit sound very far without wires. He felt that there must be a way of solving this problem.

In 1902 de Forest founded his own wireless telegraphy company. In a short time his company began to supply apparatus for ocean-going ships and for the U. S. Government.

The newspapers carried headlines when de

Forest proved that it was actually possible to telegraph over seven miles without wires. Gradually the distance became longer.

De Forest equipment was installed in several parts of the country. The distance was gradually extended to 180 miles and next to 300 miles. By now de Forest had made many improvements in his wireless equipment, and it was setting the world records for distance.

In 1904 de Forest was invited to make wireless exhibitions at the St. Louis Exhibition or world's fair. The tower which he built, one hundred feet high, was the tallest structure on the grounds.

About this time de Forest obtained many patents on his inventions. He had begun secret experiments in his laboratory with a little black box. This box, which he called an audion, led to an invention, later considered one of the twenty greatest inventions of all time.

In 1907 de Forest patented the audion, which is sometimes called a vacuum tube. The patent for this device is considered one of the most valuable patents ever issued by the United States Patent Office.

The audion was the first important electronic tube ever invented. It greatly extended wireless communication, so that messages could be sent thousands of miles over both sea and land. It improved reception, so that messages could be interpreted with great clarity.

From the audion, tubes were developed for use in both radio and television. From the same source, beams were developed to guide aviators in guiding airplanes, and sonar echoes were developed to warn sailors of rocks and other dangers at sea. Also from this tube, instruments were devised to measure cosmic rays and atomic radiation. In short, the audion was the foundation of today's great electronics industry.

In 1907 the U. S. Navy arranged for de Forest to equip a fleet of navy ships with wireless or radio telephones. The captains hoped to be able to converse when their ships were five or ten miles apart. After the equipment was installed, however, they found that they could talk with one another when they were on ships as far as twenty-two miles apart.

Soon de Forest was invited to install apparatus for making long-distance radiotelephone tests from the famous Eiffel Tower in Paris, France. His broadcasts could be heard in Italy, 500 miles away. The success of these broadcasts convinced him that it would be possible to telephone from New York to Paris without wires.

In the meantime many ships at sea were being equipped with radiotelephones. Then, in case of disaster, these ships could broadcast distress signals. Thus many lives were saved that otherwise would have been lost.

In the succeeding years, de Forest worked on new inventions and improved some of his old ones. Sometime he hoped to be able to broadcast music from the Metropolitan Opera House in New York.

In 1910 de Forest made arrangements to broadcast a program by the great Italian singer, Enrico Caruso. In this program, people could listen either by means of wireless telephones or ordinary telephones. Newspapers carried accounts of this wireless marvel, which many people could scarcely believe.

By 1916 de Forest opened a station to broadcast by radio. At first his broadcasts could be heard only for a few miles, but he gradually extended the distance. Finally, he refined the equipment until his broadcasts could be heard a hundred or more miles. All the while, improvements were made in wireless telephones, which were more and more widely used.

On election night in November, 1916, de Forest broadcast news of the Presidential election between Woodrow Wilson and Charles Evans Hughes. He left the station open until 11 o'clock at night in order to keep people informed.

While de Forest was making these advances in radio, he became interested in motion pictures. By 1923 he invented a method for sound-on-film which he demonstrated in New York City.

Radio . . . television . . . sound motion pictures . . . long-distance telephones . . . transcontinental telegraphy . . . controllers . . . computers . . . radar . . . music recordings and reproductions . . . electric phonographs . . . automation—all these forms of communication that millions of people use and enjoy every day are due to the inventive genius of Lee de Forest.

In 1950 de Forest released an autobiography, entitled "Father of Radio," which tells the story of his life and his work. Scientists and journalists had honored him with this title for many years. Many also had called him "The Grandfather of Television," because of the great contribution of his audion tube. Scientists everywhere realized that this tube, in fact, served as a foundation for the modern electronics industry.

De Forest lived to see a multibillion-dollar electronics industry, employing more than a million persons, develop from his invention of the vacuum tube. He made hundreds of inventions, but he is remembered chiefly for this original tube, which paved the way for the modern tubes widely used today.

Lee de Forest received many honors during his lifetime. He was given awards, medals, and plaques. He received the Cross of the Legion of Honor from the French Government. He received honorary degrees, including the degree of Doctor of Science from Yale University. He was honored by many writers and speakers, who reminded the world of the importance of his work. He was even praised by his old rivals.

All through his life de Forest felt that there was something ahead to create. He obtained greater thrill from creation than from the honors bestowed upon him. Fortunately he lived to see people derive many benefits from his inventions.

When de Forest died in 1961 at the age of eighty-seven, he was still experimenting and inventing. He still was eager to contribute to the scientific progress which he had started and saw everywhere around him.

More About This Book

WHEN LEE DE FOREST LIVED

1873   LEE DE FOREST WAS BORN IN COUNCIL BLUFFS, IOWA, AUGUST 26.

There were thirty-seven states in the Union.

Ulysses S. Grant was President.

The population of the country was about 42,920,000.

1873- LEE LIVED WITH HIS PARENTS AND GREW UP IN
1890   IOWA AND ALABAMA.

Alexander G. Bell invented the telephone, 1876.

The first electric street railway in the United States was operated, 1885.

Thomas Edison invented the motion picture camera, 1889.

1890- LEE ATTENDED SCHOOL IN NEW ENGLAND AND
1899   EARNED HIS PH.D. DEGREE FROM YALE.

Henry Ford built his first gas engine, 1893.

Roentgen discovered X-rays, 1895.

The Spanish-American War was fought, 1898.

1899- 1922	DE FOREST INVENTED THE AUDION AND STAGED FIRST RADIO BROADCAST.

Wilbur and Orville Wright flew the first heavier-than-air aircraft, 1903.

The Panama Canal was completed and opened to world traffic, 1914.

World War I was fought, 1914-1918.

1922- 1949	DE FOREST HELPED TO DEVELOP TALKING MOTION PICTURES AND TELEVISION.

The first full-length talking motion picture was made, 1927.

Wiley Post flew a small airplane around the world, 1933.

World War II was fought, 1939-1945.

1949- 1961	DE FOREST WROTE HIS AUTOBIOGRAPHY AND CONTINUED HIS EXPERIMENTAL WORK.

The Korean War was fought, 1950-1953.

Nautilus, the first atomic-powered submarine, was completed, 1954.

Explorer I, first U. S. earth satellite, was launched, 1958.

Alaska and Hawaii became states in the Union, 1959.

194

1961 LEE DE FOREST DIED IN HOLLYWOOD, CALIFORNIA, JUNE 30.

There were fifty states in the Union.

John F. Kennedy was President.

The population of the United States was about 180,150,000.

DO YOU REMEMBER?

1. Why did Lee become puzzled and excited during a trip down Main Street?

2. Why was Lee especially interested in the calliope in the circus?

3. Why did the de Forest family move from Iowa to Alabama?

4. How did the men make bricks for putting up Stone Hall at Talladega College?

5. How did the de Forests get a house of their own after they moved to Talladega?

6. What did Mr. de Forest tell his children about stars in the sky?

7. Why was Lee greatly disturbed when several big boys came to the river?

8. How did Lee earn money with a new silver plating outfit which he ordered?

9. How did Lee and Charles construct a locomotive in their back yard?

10. How did Lee design and build a small blast furnace in the yard?

11. How did Lee secure permission from his father to become a scientist and inventor?

12. What problems did Lee face while attending Yale Sheffield Scientific School?

13. Why did the audion tube which de Forest invented mean so much to the world?

14. What honors did de Forest receive for his audion tube and other inventions?

IT'S FUN TO LOOK UP THESE THINGS

1. What is electricity and how was it first discovered?

2. How does static electricity differ from current or flowing electricity?

3. Which form of electricity is manufactured and widely used in the world?

4. What are electrons and where may they be found around you?

5. How is electronics concerned with broadcasting by radio and television?

6. What are the leading parts of a radio or television set?

INTERESTING THINGS YOU CAN DO

1. Find out how Benjamin Franklin performed an electrical experiment with a kite.

2. Make a list of famous scientists who helped to discover electricity.

3. Explain how doctors make use of X-rays in diagnosing and treating diseases.

4. Read what a vacuum tube is like and explain it to your classmates.

5. Name several electronic devices which are widely used today.

6. Explain radar and tell why it is important in protecting airplanes and ships.

7. Prepare a report telling what takes place in a broadcasting station.

OTHER BOOKS YOU MAY ENJOY READING

Research Adventures for Young Scientists, George Barr. McGraw-Hill.

Safe and Simple Projects with Electricity, Charles Neal. Childrens Press.

Small Motors You Can Make, John Michael. Van Nostrand.

Sound and Its Reproduction, Jerome S. Meyer. World Publishing Co.

Story Behind Great Inventions, Elizabeth Montgomery. Dodd.

Thomas Edison: Boy Inventor, Sue Guthridge. Trade and School Editions, Bobbs-Merrill.

INTERESTING WORDS IN THIS BOOK

anticipate (ăn tĭs′ĭ pāt) : look forward to

antics (ăn′tĭks) : capers, stunts

astronomy (ăs trŏn′ŏ mĭ) : science that deals with the heavenly bodies

blast furnace: special furnace used to smelt metals

compressor (kŏm prĕs′ẽr) : pump used to condense something, as air at a filling station

crevice (krĕv′ĭs) : narrow opening, crack

electronics (ė lĕk′trŏn′ĭks) : branch of electricity that deals with electrons or tiny negative charges of electricity

firebox: part of a steam locomotive in which the fuel is burned

frequency (wave length) : number of vibrations per second, as in the strings of a musical instrument; also number of cycles of alternating current per second

friction (frĭk′shŭn) : resistance that comes from rubbing or sliding, as when one part of machinery moves over another

generator (jĕn′ẽr ā′tẽr) : dynamo, machine for converting mechanical energy into electricity

hydrogen (hī′drȯ jĕn) : colorless, tasteless gas, which burns readily and is one of the lightest substances known

inquisitive (ĭn kwĭz′ĭ tĭv) : curious, wanting to know

intricate (ĭn′trĭ kĭt) : complicated, hard to understand or follow

miniature (mĭn′ĭ ȧ tŭr) : tiny

molten (mōl′tĕn) : melted, as a metal

physics (fĭz′ĭks) : science that deals with mechanics, heat, light, sound, and electricity

199

piston (pĭs'tŭn) : sliding part that moves back and forth in the cylinder of a steam engine to produce motion

pressure (prĕsh'ẽr) : force that tends to cause something to move

ravenous (răv'ĕn ŭs) : eager for food

reversing lever (rė vûrs'ĭng lē'vẽr) : part which may be moved to make a locomotive or other motorized vehicle go backward

sluice (slōōs) : ditch or other artificial passage for water, fitted with a gate or valve to regulate the flow of the water

smelt (smĕlt) : melt ore in order to remove the valuable portion

sonar (sō'när) : apparatus that locates underwater objects by emitting high-frequency sound waves which are reflected back

transmit (trăns mĭt') : send signals through space which are intended for a distant receiver

valve (vălv) : mechanical device in a tube or pipe which may be opened or closed to regulate the flow of a liquid or gas

vendor (vĕn'dẽr) : salesman

weld (wĕld) : unite pieces of metal, as iron, by heating and hammering

200

UNIVERSITY SCHOOL
LIBRARY
KENT, OHIO

Childhood

OF FAMOUS AMERICANS

CHILDHOOD
OF FAMOUS
AMERICANS

COLONIAL DAYS

JAMES OGLETHORPE, *Parks*
JOHN ALDEN, *Burt*
MYLES STANDISH, *Stevenson*
PETER STUYVESANT, *Widdemer*
POCAHONTAS, *Seymour*
PONTIAC, *Peckham*
SQUANTO, *Stevenson*
VIRGINIA DARE, *Stevenson*
WILLIAM BRADFORD, *Smith*
WILLIAM PENN, *Mason*

STRUGGLE for INDEPENDENCE

ANTHONY WAYNE, *Stevenson*
BEN FRANKLIN, *Stevenson*
BETSY ROSS, *Weil*
DAN MORGAN, *Bryant*
ETHAN ALLEN, *Winders*
FRANCIS MARION, *Steele*
GEORGE ROGERS CLARK, *Wilkie*
GEORGE WASHINGTON, *Stevenson*
ISRAEL PUTNAM, *Stevenson*
JOHN HANCOCK, *Cleven*
JOHN PAUL JONES, *Snow*
MARTHA WASHINGTON, *Wagoner*
MOLLY PITCHER, *Stevenson*
NATHAN HALE, *Stevenson*
NATHANAEL GREENE, *Peckham*
PATRICK HENRY, *Barton*
PAUL REVERE, *Stevenson*
TOM JEFFERSON, *Monsell*

EARLY NATIONAL GROWTH

ABIGAIL ADAMS, *Wagoner*
ALEC HAMILTON, *Higgins*
ANDY JACKSON, *Stevenson*
DAN WEBSTER, *Smith*
DEWITT CLINTON, *Widdemer*
DOLLY MADISON, *Monsell*
ELI WHITNEY, *Snow*
ELIAS HOWE, *Corcoran*
FRANCIS SCOTT KEY, *Stevenson*
HENRY CLAY, *Monsell*
JAMES FENIMORE COOPER, *Winders*
JAMES MONROE, *Widdemer*
JOHN AUDUBON, *Mason*
JOHN F. KENNEDY, *Frisbee*
JOHN JACOB ASTOR, *Anderson*
JOHN MARSHALL, *Monsell*
JOHN QUINCY ADAMS, *Weil*
LUCRETIA MOTT, *Burnett*
MATTHEW CALBRAITH PERRY, *Scharbach*
NANCY HANKS, *Stevenson*
NOAH WEBSTER, *Higgins*
OLIVER HAZARD PERRY, *Long*
RACHEL JACKSON, *Govan*
ROBERT FULTON, *Henry*
SAMUEL MORSE, *Snow*
SEQUOYAH, *Snow*
STEPHEN DECATUR, *Smith*
STEPHEN FOSTER, *Higgins*
WASHINGTON IRVING, *Widdemer*
ZACK TAYLOR, *Wilkie*

WESTWARD MOVEMENT

BRIGHAM YOUNG, *Jordan and Frisbee*
BUFFALO BILL, *Stevenson*
DANIEL BOONE, *Stevenson*
DAVY CROCKETT, *Parks*
GAIL BORDEN, *Paradis*
JED SMITH, *Burt*
JESSIE FREMONT, *Wagoner*